odd and even

+	9	2	4	7	3
0					
6					
7					
4					
9					

odd and even

The sums are:
odd numbers only
even numbers only
even and odd numbers mixed

even addends

+					

even addends

The sums are:
odd numbers only
even numbers only
even and odd numbers mixed

odd and even

+	9	8	7	6	5
8					
7					
6					
5					
4					

odd and even

The sums are:
odd numbers only
even numbers only
even and odd numbers mixed

odd addends

+					

odd addends

The sums are:
odd numbers only
even numbers only
even and odd numbers mixed

odd addends

+	9	7	5	3	1
0					
2					
4					
6					
8					

even addends

The sums are:
odd numbers only
even numbers only
even and odd numbers mixed

even addends

+					

odd addends

The sums are:
odd numbers only
even numbers only
even and odd numbers mixed

Find the sums. Fill in the charts.

+	3	13	23
5			
15			
25			

How does this chart help you with 38 - 23 = ☐ ?

+	7	5	9
8			
18			
28			

Let the filled-in chart help you with 25 - 7 and other subtraction problems.

+	7	17	27
4			
34			
74			

+	1	10	100
9			
99			
999			

Extra Hard

+	32	
9		
6		41

Write your own addends. Use numbers > 20. Find their sums.

+		

+		

+		
12	5	
15	8	

+		

+		

Ref: *Lab Sheet Annotations*, pages 53 and 54.

●●●●● C-38

+	123	106	89	72	55	38	21
123							
106							
89							
72							
55							
38							
21							

Find some patterns of your
own in these addition tables.

Finish these addition tables.

What is special about the
numbers that go this way? ↗↙

They are _____

What is the difference
between one number and
the next as you go down
the columns? ↓

The difference is _____

+	12	23	34	45	56	67	78	89
89								
82								
75								
68								
61								
54								
47								
40								

What is the difference between one number
and the next as you go this way? ↗
The difference is _____

The difference between
one number and the next
as you go down the

columns is _____

The difference between
one number and the next
as you go across the

row is _____

What is the difference
between one number and
next as you go this way? ↗↘

The difference is _____

Ref: *Lab Sheet Annotations*, page 53.

Name _____   Date _____

7 | 6
4 | 9

The grid on the left tells you what numbers you
have to add in order to fill in the frames below.
The designs are your clues.

12 | 3
5 | 18

8 | 5

The two frames that have been filled in tell you
how to finish the grid.

Ref: *Lab Sheet Annotations*, page 55.

Name _____ Date _____

6, 2, 0, and 7 are one-digit numerals.
13, 64, and 50 are two-digit numerals.
637, 406, and 500 are three-digit numerals.

The <u>one-digit</u> <u>numeral</u> for the <u>largest</u> number of units is the numeral [ ].

The <u>one-digit</u> <u>numeral</u> for the <u>smallest</u> number of units is the numeral [ ].

[ ] names the <u>smallest</u> number > 9 that can be written in <u>two digits</u>.

99 names the _____ number that can be written in <u>two digits</u>.

Knowing something about many-digit numerals helps us in writing sums greater than nine.

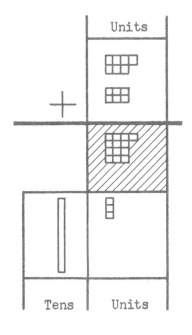

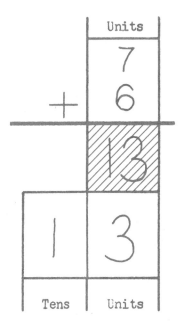

9   5   8   7   44
+7   +8   +9   +6   +8

Ref: *Lab Sheet Annotations*, page 55.

Name _____ Date _____

In the shaded boxes collect all the units in the units' column and all the
tens in the tens' column. If there are more than 9 units in the units' place,
exchange for tens and units. If there are more than 9 tens in the tens' place,
exchange for hundreds and tens.

Examples:

```
      52          43          74
    +29         +85         +66
    ┌7│11┐      ┌12│8┐       ┌13│10┐
    └─┤8 1┘     └12 8┘       ┤14│0 ┤
                             └─ 140┘
```

Now finish these problems:

```
   64          37          28          57          55
 +25        +47         +59         +33         +29
```

```
   64          82          78          66          43
 +73        +30         +81         +63         +85
```

```
   76          67          98          88          99
 +87        +43         +44         +55         +24
```

Ref: *Lab Sheet Annotations*, page 56.   ●●●●● C-42

```
   4 5 3
 + 3 5 6
```
7	0	9
8	0	9

H T U

```
   7 7 7
 + 1 4 2
```
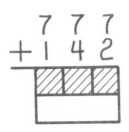

```
   4 6 4
 + 4 7 4
```
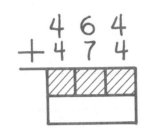

```
   3 5 3
 + 2 7 4
```
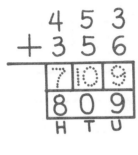

```
   5 2 9
 + 3 4 8
```
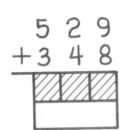

```
   6 3 6
 + 3 5 5
```
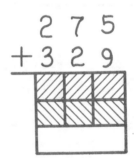

```
   4 4 3
 + 4 4 7
```

```
   1 5 8
 + 6 3 9
```

```
   2 7 5
 + 3 2 9
```

```
   6 5 4
 + 2 6 7
```

```
   3 4 5
 + 5 7 6
```
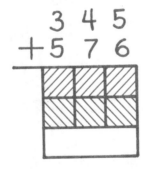

```
   2 4 1
 + 4 7 9
```
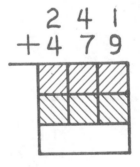

```
   8 6 5
 + 4 7 6
```
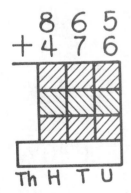

Th H T U

```
   5 7 9
 + 6 4 3
```

```
   7 5 5
 + 7 5 5
```

```
   9 4 6
 +   9 8
```
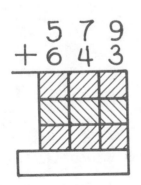

Ref: *Lab Sheet Annotations*, page 56.

Name _____ Date _____

A Shorter Way of Adding
A teaching page

$$35 + 47 = \boxed{}$$

$\boxed{1}$ 35 $+47$ $\overline{\quad 2}$	5 and 7 have already been added. 12, their sum, equals 1 ten plus 2 units Find where the 1 ten is written. Find where the 2 units are written.
$\boxed{1}$ 35 $+47$ $\overline{\quad 2}$	Now add up __all__ the tens.

$\boxed{}$
46
$+28$

$6 + 8 = 14$ Where do you write the units?

Where do you write the tens?

Add up __all__ the tens.

$\boxed{}$	$\boxed{}$	$\boxed{}$	$\boxed{}$	$\boxed{}$
29 $+55$	143 $+28$	637 $+134$	533 $+257$	182 $+508$
$\boxed{}$	$\boxed{}$	$\boxed{}$	$\boxed{}$	$\boxed{}$
348 $+524$	379 $+420$	666 $+226$	734 $+229$	203 $+407$

Ref: *Lab Sheet Annotations*, page 57.

☐
382
+427
‾‾‾‾

☐
541
+376
‾‾‾‾

☐
444
+375
‾‾‾‾

☐
724
+146
‾‾‾‾

☐☐
245
+255
‾‾‾‾

☐
372
+ 85
‾‾‾‾

☐
439
+ 58
‾‾‾‾

☐☐
439
+ 78
‾‾‾‾

☐☐
599
+ 99
‾‾‾‾

34
+ 27
‾‾‾‾
⌞6⌟1

48
+45
‾‾‾

76
+38
‾‾‾

57
+35
‾‾‾

124
+128
‾‾‾‾

365
+325
‾‾‾‾

277
+322
‾‾‾‾

463
+253
‾‾‾‾

624
+280
‾‾‾‾

325
+495
‾‾‾‾

Ref: *Lab Sheet Annotations*, page 57.

● ● ● ● ●   C-45

A   B

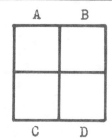

C   D

Discover from the grid on the left what numerals or designs go into the frames below. Write them in.

B+C   A+B   A+C+D

A+C   B+D   A+B+C   B+C+D   A+B+D

A   B

C   D

Put your own numerals in the grid on the left. Then fill in the empty frames with the correct numerals.

A+B   A+C   A+D   B+C   B+D   C+D

A+B+C   A+B+D   A+C+D   B+C+D   A+B+C+D

A   B

C   D

Look at the finished frames below. These are your clues to help you finish the grid on the left and the other empty frames.

 28

A+B   A+C   A+D   52 B+C   32 B+D   C+D

 61

A+B+C   A+B+D   A+C+D   B+C+D   A+B+C+D

Ref: *Lab Sheet Annotations*, page 58.

$$63 \xrightarrow{\;\square\;} 69 \xrightarrow{\;\hexagon\;} 99$$

$$99 - \hexagon = 63$$

$$\begin{array}{r} 99 \\ -\,63 \\ \hline \end{array} \qquad \begin{array}{r} 63 \\ + \\ \hline 99 \end{array}$$

$$123 \xrightarrow{\;\square\;} 130 \xrightarrow{\;\hexagon\;} 180 \xrightarrow{\;\bigcirc\;} 380$$

$$123 + \hexagon = 380$$

$$\begin{array}{r} 380 \\ -\,123 \\ \hline \end{array} \qquad \begin{array}{r} 380 \\ - \\ \hline 123 \end{array} \qquad \begin{array}{r} 123 \\ + \\ \hline 380 \end{array}$$

$$257 \xrightarrow{\;\hexagon\;} 260 \xrightarrow{\;\bigcirc\;} 300 \xrightarrow{\;\square\;} 700$$

$$82 \xrightarrow{\;\hexagon\;} 90 \xrightarrow{\;\bigcirc\;} 100 \xrightarrow{\;\square\;} 1000$$

$$70 \xrightarrow{\;\hexagon\;} 80 \xrightarrow{\;\bigcirc\;} 380 \xrightarrow{\;\square\;} 1380$$

$$62 \xrightarrow{\;\hexagon\;} 71 \xrightarrow{\;\bigcirc\;} 121 \xrightarrow{\;\square\;} 421$$

$$6 \xrightarrow{\;\hexagon\;} 12 \xrightarrow{\;\bigcirc\;} 82 \xrightarrow{\;\square\;} 382$$

$$10 \xrightarrow{\;\hexagon\;} 12 \xrightarrow{\;\bigcirc\;} 82 \xrightarrow{\;\square\;} 382$$

$$77 \xrightarrow{\;\hexagon\;} 80 \xrightarrow{\;\bigcirc\;} 170 \xrightarrow{\;\square\;} 770$$

$$44 \xrightarrow{\;7\;} \square \xrightarrow{\;60\;} \bigcirc \xrightarrow{\;300\;} \hexagon$$

$$328 \xrightarrow{\;5\;} \square \xrightarrow{\;\bigcirc\;} 403 \xrightarrow{\;300\;} \hexagon$$

Ref: *Lab Sheet Annotations*, pages 63 and 73.

●●●●● D-19

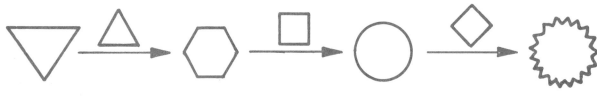

285 ▲ → ⬡ 289 □ 40 → ○ 329 ◇ → 429

309 ▲ → ⬡ 313 □ → ○ 353 ◇ → 853

43 ▲ → ⬡ □ → ○ ◇ → 720

60 ▲ → ⬡ □ → ○ ◇ → ✳

▽ ▲ → ⬡ □ → ○ ◇ → ✳

▽ ▲ → ⬡ □ → ○ ◇ → ✳

300 ← ▲ ⬡ ← □ ○ ← ◇ 716

147 ← ▲ ⬡ ← □ ○ ← ◇ 435

▽ ← ▲ ⬡ ← □ ○ ← ◇ ✳

Ref: *Lab Sheet Annotations*, pages 63 and 73.

• • • • • D-20

Which problem is easier to do?

43 – 17	or	46 – 20
55 – 28	or	57 – 30
91 – 50	or	90 – 49
72 – 48	or	74 – 50
67 – 40	or	64 – 37
75 – 30	or	71 – 26

136 – 79   or   137 – 80   or   157 – 100

354 – 186   or   358 – 190   or   368 – 200

Use >, =, or< to make true sentences:

34 – 19 ---- 35 – 20

56 – 20 ⎯⎯ 52 – 16

48 – 30 ⎯⎯ 46 – 28

84 – 57 ⎯⎯ 87 – 60

153 – 77 ⎯⎯ 156 – 80

156 – 80 ⎯⎯ 176 – 100

Ref: *Lab Sheet Annotations*, pages 63 and 74.

• • • • • D-21

Name _____ Date _____

$34 - 18 = \boxed{} - 20 = \hexagon$

$64 - 37 = \boxed{} - 40 = \hexagon$

$55 - 29 = \boxed{} - 30 = \hexagon$

$42 - 16 = \boxed{} - 20 = \hexagon$

$91 - 64 = \boxed{} - 70 = \hexagon$

$44 - 28 = \boxed{} - 30 = \hexagon$

$82 - 65 = \boxed{} - 70 = \hexagon$

$73 - 47 = \boxed{} - 50 = \hexagon$

$66 - 28 = \boxed{} - 30 = \hexagon$

$116 - 47 = \boxed{} - 50 = \hexagon$

$173 - 86 = \boxed{} - 90 = \hexagon - 100 = \bigcirc$

$352 - 178 = \boxed{} - 180 = \hexagon - 200 = \bigcirc$

$264 - 189 = \boxed{} - 190 = \hexagon - 200 = \bigcirc$

$822 - 376 = \boxed{} - 380 = \hexagon - 400 = \bigcirc$

Ref: *Lab Sheet Annotations*, pages 63 and 74.

• • • • • D-22

45 ——— − 10 ⟶ ☐ ——— + 10 ⟶ ⬡

10 ——— − 10 ⟶ ☐ ——— + 10 ⟶ ⬡

573 ——— − 10 ⟶ ☐ ——— + 10 ⟶ ⬡

6 ——— − 10 ⟶ ☐ ——— + 10 ⟶ ⬡

212 ——— − 10 ⟶ ☐ ——— + 10 ⟶ ⬡

762 ——— − 10 ⟶ ☐ ——— + 10 ⟶ ⬡

308 ——— − 10 ⟶ ☐ ——— + 10 ⟶ ⬡

421 ——— − 10 ⟶ ☐ ——— + 10 ⟶ ⬡

770 ——— − 10 ⟶ ☐ ——— + 10 ⟶ ⬡

Ref: *Lab Sheet Annotations*, page 102.

●●●●● E-50

Name _____ Date _____

362 ──── + 100 ────▶ ☐ ──── − 100 ────▶ △

939 ──── + 100 ────▶ ☐ ──── − 100 ────▶ △

1,438 ──── + 100 ────▶ ☐ ──── − 100 ────▶ △

2,941 ──── + 100 ────▶ ☐ ──── − 100 ────▶ △

47 ──── + 100 ────▶ ☐ ──── − 100 ────▶ △

5 ──── + 100 ────▶ ☐ ──── − 100 ────▶ △

1,000 ──── + 100 ────▶ ☐ ──── − 100 ────▶ △

4,020 ──── + 100 ────▶ ☐ ──── − 100 ────▶ △

0 ──── + 100 ────▶ ☐ ──── − 100 ────▶ △

980 ──── + 100 ────▶ ☐ ──── − 100 ────▶ △

Ref: *Lab Sheet Annotations*, page 102.

−	9	2	8	3	7	4	6	5	
19	10								
14									
10									
16									
13									
18									
15									
12									
17									

Finish this subtraction table.

+	5								
9			15		18				
		17					26		
								30	
				17					
7				14					
12		24						26	
				10					
		18				17			
			20						

Finish this addition table.

Ref: *Lab Sheet Annotations*, page 103.

$10 + \boxed{} = 100$

$17 + \boxed{} = 100$

$\boxed{} + 30 = 100$

$\boxed{} + 32 = 100$

$100 = 90 + \boxed{}$

$100 = \boxed{} + 89$

$46 = 100 - \boxed{}$

$73 + \boxed{} = 100$

$26 = 100 - \boxed{}$

$100 - \boxed{} = 68$

$36 + \boxed{} = 100$

$200 = 18 + \boxed{}$

$1000 = 350 + \boxed{}$

$800 + \boxed{} = 1000$

$990 = 1000 - \boxed{}$

$1000 = 333 + \boxed{}$

$1000 - 586 = \boxed{}$

$1000 = \boxed{} + 948$

$1642 - 1000 = \boxed{}$

$875 + \boxed{} = 1000$

2 3
4

2 0
4 8

1 27
2 3

Ref: *Lab Sheet Annotations*, page 129.

• • • • • • F-47

Name _____ Date _____

Find the Products

X	2	4	6
2			
4			
6			

Shade in all the square numbers.

X	1	3	5
1			
3			
5			

Shade in all the square numbers.

X	3	4	5
4			
5			
6			

Shade in blue all the odd numbers.
Shade in yellow all the square numbers.

X	3	7	2
4			
6			
3			

Shade in yellow all the even numbers.

X	6	11
3		
9		

Shade in green all the numbers which have three as a factor.

X	15	10
5		
10		

Shade in yellow all numbers divisible by 20 without a remainder.

X		7
6	42	
		21

X	2	12
3		
4		

X	1	6
6		
8		

X		
	12	24
	24	48

Ref: *Lab Sheet Annotations*, page 129.

●●●●● F-48

$(1 \times 100) + (1 \times 10) + (1 \times 3) =$ ⬡100 $+$ ◯10 $+$ ☐3 $=$ ✴

$(2 \times 100) + (2 \times 10) + (2 \times 3) =$ ⬡ $+$ ◯ $+$ ☐ $=$ ✴

$(3 \times 100) + (3 \times 10) + (3 \times 3) =$ ⬡ $+$ ◯ $+$ ☐ $=$ ✴

$4 \times (100 + 10 + 3) =$ ⬡400 $+$ ◯ $+$ ☐12 $=$ ✴

$5 \times (100 + 10 + 3) =$ ⬡ $+$ ◯ $+$ ☐ $=$ ✴

$6 \times (100 + 10 + 3) =$ ⬡ $+$ ◯ $+$ ☐ $=$ ✴

$7 \times (100 + 10 + 3) =$ ⬡ $+$ ◯ $+$ ☐ $=$ ✴

$3 \times (50 + 7) =$ ⬡150 $+$ ◯ $=$ ✴

$5 \times (20 + 4) =$ ⬡ $+$ ◯20 $=$ ✴

$7 \times (10 + 3) =$ ⬡ $+$ ◯ $=$ ☐

$(8 \times 10) + (8 \times 4) =$ ⬡ $+$ ◯32 $=$ ☐

$4 \times 27 =$ ⬡80 $+$ ◯ $=$ ☐

$3 \times 56 =$ ⬡ $+$ ◯ $=$ ☐

Ref: *Lab Sheet Annotations*, page 130.   ●●●●● F-49

Name

(Top left)

$160 + 16 = 8 \times \bigcirc$

$3 \times 14 = 30 + \hexagon$

$5 \times 36 = \hexagon + 30 = \square$

$6 \times 23 = \hexagon + 18 = \square$

$7 \times 18 = 70 + \hexagon = \square$

$4 \times 17 = 40 + \hexagon = \square$

(Top right)

$8 \times 12 = 16 + \square = \square$

$9 \times 33 = 27 + \square = \square$

$7 \times 55 = 35 + \square = \bigcirc$

$6 \times 44 = \square + 240 = \bigcirc$

$6 \times 64 = 24 + \square = \bigcirc$

(Bottom left)

$5 \times 10 + \boxed{5 \times 3} = 5 \times \square$

$3 \times 100 + \boxed{3 \times 6} = 3 \times \square$

$7 \times 10 + 7 \times 4 = \square \times 14$

$6 \times \square + 6 \times 2 = 6 \times 12$

$4 \times \square + 4 \times 5 = 4 \times 105$

$8 \times 10 + \square \times 1 = 8 \times 11$

$\square \times 10 + \square \times 7 = 3 \times 17$

(Bottom right)

$40 + 24 = 4 \times \bigcirc$

$60 + 15 = \bigcirc \times 25$

$70 + 21 = \bigcirc \times 13$

$60 + 30 = 6 \times \bigcirc$

Ref: *Lab Sheet Annotations*, page 130.

●●●●● F–50

If my name is (1) ——→ then what is my name?

and what is my name?

What is my name?

If my name is (1) ——→ what is my name ?

What is my name?

What is my name?

If my name is (1)

Ref: *Lab Sheet Annotations*, page 158.

•••••• H-43

w says: "I am so short.

p is 4 times as tall as I

am, and b is ☐ times as

tall as I am."

p says: "w is only _____ as

tall as I am, and b is _____

as tall as I am."

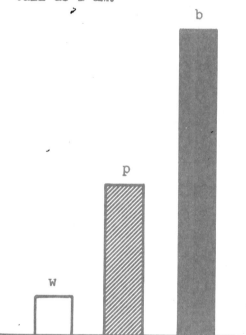

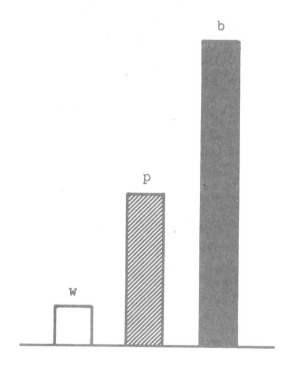

b says: "Look at me. I am

the tallest. p is _____ my

size and w is _____ my size."

Ref: *Lab Sheet Annotations*, page 158.

● ● ● ● ● H-44

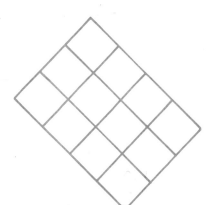 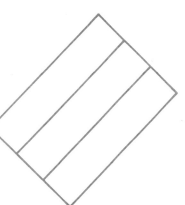 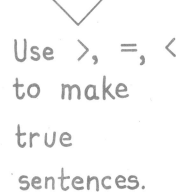

$\frac{1}{12}$ of 12 = $\boxed{1}$

$\frac{2}{12}$ of 12 = $\boxed{2}$

$\frac{3}{12}$ of 12 = $\boxed{3}$

$\frac{4}{12}$ of 12 = $\boxed{4}$

$\frac{6}{12}$ of 12 = $\boxed{6}$

$\frac{8}{12}$ of 12 = $\boxed{8}$

$\frac{9}{12}$ of 12 = $\boxed{9}$

$\frac{12}{12}$ of 12 = $\boxed{12}$

$\frac{1}{3}$ of 12 = $\boxed{4}$

$\frac{2}{3}$ of 12 = $\boxed{8}$

$\frac{3}{3}$ of 12 = $\boxed{16}$

$\frac{1}{4} \times 12 = \boxed{}$

$\frac{2}{4} \times 12 = \boxed{}$

$\frac{3}{4} \times 12 = \boxed{}$

$\frac{4}{4} \times 12 = \boxed{}$

Use >, =, < to make true sentences.

$\frac{1}{3}$ $\frac{2}{6}$

$\frac{2}{4}$ $\frac{2}{3}$

$\frac{4}{12}$ $\frac{5}{12}$

$\frac{3}{6}$ $\frac{1}{3}$

$\frac{6}{12}$ $\frac{3}{6}$

$\left(\frac{1}{2} \times 12\right) + \left(\frac{6}{12} \times 12\right) = \boxed{}$

$\left(\frac{1}{3} \times 12\right) + \left(\frac{1}{4} \times 12\right) = \boxed{}$

$\left(\frac{2}{3} \times 12\right) + \left(\frac{2}{12} \times 12\right) = \boxed{}$

Name _____ Date _____

Which is more?

$\frac{1}{3} \times 12$ or $\frac{1}{6} \times 12$

$\frac{1}{2} \times 6$ or $\frac{1}{3} \times 6$

$\frac{1}{9} \times 9$ or $\frac{1}{3} \times 9$

$\frac{1}{5} \times 10$ or $\frac{1}{2} \times 10$

$\frac{2}{5} \times 15$ or $\frac{1}{3} \times 15$

$\frac{10}{100} \times 100$ or $\frac{1}{2} \times 10$

$\frac{1}{3} \times 6$ or $\frac{1}{4} \times 8$

$\frac{7}{10} \times 10$ or $\frac{1}{2} \times 16$

Name_____ Date_____

Label each point on the numb

$$\frac{0}{3} \quad \frac{1}{3} \quad \frac{3}{3}$$

Use the number line to solve the problems below.

$\frac{2}{3} + \frac{3}{3} = \square$ $2 \times \frac{2}{3} = \square$

$\frac{5}{3} + \square = 2$ $\square = 4 \times \frac{2}{3}$

$\frac{7}{3} - \frac{7}{3} = \square$ $\frac{6}{3} \div \frac{2}{3} = \square$

$\frac{8}{3} - \square = 1$ $\square \times \frac{1}{3} = 2$

$\frac{2}{3} = \square + \square$

Ref: *Lab Sheet Annotations*, page 158.   ● ● ● ● ● H-47

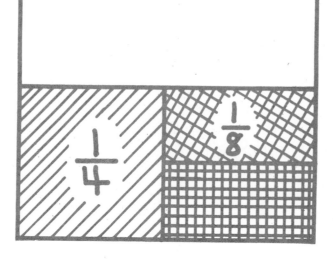

$\frac{1}{2} + \frac{1}{4} + \frac{2}{8} = \square$

$1 = \frac{1}{2} + \square$

$\square = \frac{1}{4} + \frac{1}{4}$

$\frac{1}{8} + \frac{1}{8} = \square$

$4 \times \frac{1}{4} = \square$

$\square = \frac{1}{4} \times 4$

$3 \times \frac{1}{4} = \square$

$3 \times 4 = \square$

$2\frac{1}{2} \times 4 = \square$

Name _____ Date _____

FRACTIONS ON THE NUMBER LINE

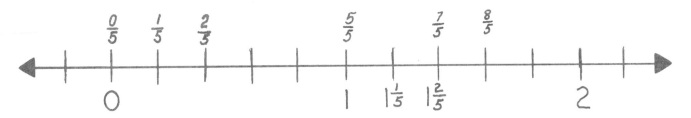

Finish labeling the points on the number line.

Can you solve the problems below? Use the number line to help you.

$\frac{4}{5} + \frac{5}{5} = \boxed{}$

$\frac{9}{5} + \boxed{} = 2$

$\frac{11}{5} - \frac{7}{5} = \boxed{}$

$\frac{13}{5} - \boxed{} = 1$

$\frac{2}{5} = \boxed{} + \boxed{}$

$2 \times \frac{3}{5} = \boxed{}$

$\boxed{} = 4 \times \frac{2}{5}$

How many $\frac{2}{5}$'s in $\frac{10}{5}$?

$\frac{10}{5} \div \frac{2}{5} = \boxed{}$

$\frac{2}{10} = \boxed{\dfrac{}{5}}$

Make up some problems of your own.

Ref: *Lab Sheet Annotations*, page 158.

●●●●● H-49

Name _____ Date _____

$$\frac{1}{3}\ \frac{1}{3}\ \frac{1}{3}$$

$$\frac{1}{2}\ \frac{1}{2}$$

$$\frac{1}{6}\ \frac{1}{6}\ \frac{1}{6}\ \frac{1}{6}\ \frac{1}{6}\ \frac{1}{6}$$

$$\frac{3}{3} = 1 \qquad\qquad \frac{2}{2} = 1 \qquad\qquad \frac{6}{6} = 1$$

Put loops around all the names for 1.

$$\frac{7}{7} \qquad \frac{50}{51} \qquad \frac{81}{18}$$

one

sixteen sixths

$$\frac{6}{5}$$

1

$$\frac{10}{10}$$

seven sevenths

$$\frac{90}{45} \qquad \frac{44}{88} \qquad \frac{90}{90} \qquad \frac{300}{300}$$

Write some more names for 1.

Ref: *Lab Sheet Annotations*, page 160.

● ● ● ● ● H-50

Name _____ Date _____

Put loops around all the names for $\frac{1}{2}$.

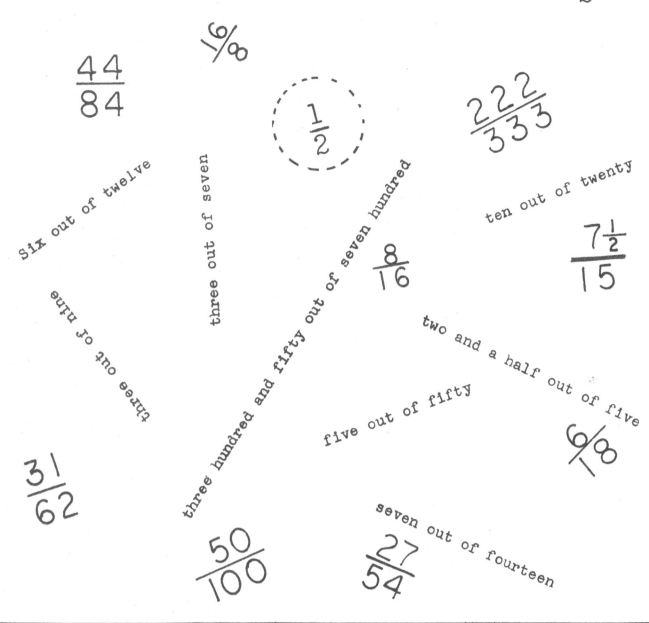

$\frac{16}{8}$

$\frac{44}{84}$

$\frac{222}{333}$

$\frac{1}{2}$

Six out of twelve

three out of seven

three hundred and fifty out of seven hundred

ten out of twenty

$7\frac{1}{2}$ over 15

$\frac{8}{16}$

three out of nine

two and a half out of five

five out of fifty

$\frac{6}{8}$

$\frac{31}{62}$

$\frac{50}{100}$

$\frac{27}{54}$

seven out of fourteen

Write some more names for $\frac{1}{2}$.

Ref: *Lab Sheet Annotations*, page 160.

● ● ● ● ● H-51

Name _____   Date _____

Make true sentences using $>$, $=$, or $<$

$\dfrac{3}{2}\ >\ \dfrac{1}{2}$ $\dfrac{6}{11}\qquad\dfrac{1}{2}$

$\dfrac{40}{80}\qquad\dfrac{1}{2}$ $\bigcirc\!\!\!\!\!\!\!\hexagon\ =\ \dfrac{1}{2}$

$\dfrac{7}{9}\qquad\dfrac{1}{2}$ $\dfrac{1}{2}\ >\ \bigcirc$

$\dfrac{6}{13}\qquad\dfrac{1}{2}$ $\dfrac{1}{2}\ <\ \hexagon$

$\dfrac{6}{12}\qquad\dfrac{1}{2}$ $\dfrac{1}{2}\ >\ \bigcirc$

$\dfrac{20}{40}\qquad\dfrac{1}{2}$ $\hexagon\ >\ \dfrac{1}{2}$

$\dfrac{12}{9}\qquad\dfrac{1}{2}$ $\dfrac{1}{2}\ =\ \bigcirc$

$\hexagon\ <\ \dfrac{1}{2}$

Make up more problems about $\dfrac{1}{2}$.

Use $=$, $>$, $<$.

Ref: *Lab Sheet Annotations*, pages 160 and 161.

●●●●● H-52

Name _____ Date _____

Find the tricky names for ③, ④, ⑤, and ⑥.

$$\frac{33}{11}$$

$$\frac{50}{10}$$

$$\frac{27}{9}$$

$$\frac{30}{10}$$

$$\frac{8}{2}$$

$$\frac{15}{5}$$

$$\frac{330}{110}$$

③

④

⑤

⑥

$$\frac{18}{3}$$

$$\frac{16}{4}$$

$$\frac{36}{9}$$

$$\frac{35}{7}$$

$$\frac{18}{4}$$

$$\frac{28}{7}$$

$$\frac{808}{202}$$

$$\frac{100}{500}$$ $$\frac{300}{100}$$

Write some of your own.

Ref: *Lab Sheet Annotations*, pages 160 and 161.

•••••• H-53

Use $=$, $>$, and $<$ to make true sentences.

$\dfrac{1}{3}$ $\dfrac{1}{2}$

$\dfrac{1}{4}$ $\dfrac{1}{2}$

$\dfrac{1}{3}$ $\dfrac{1}{4}$

$\dfrac{1}{5}$ $\dfrac{1}{3}$

$\dfrac{1}{4}$ $\dfrac{1}{5}$

$\dfrac{1}{6}$ $\dfrac{1}{5}$

$\dfrac{1}{3}$ $\dfrac{1}{6}$

$\dfrac{1}{3}$ $\dfrac{2}{6}$

$\dfrac{1}{2}$ $\dfrac{3}{4}$

$\dfrac{2}{4}$ $\dfrac{1}{2}$

How many $\dfrac{1}{2}$'s in 1?

$1 \div \dfrac{1}{2} = \boxed{}$

How many $\dfrac{1}{2}$'s in 2?

$2 \div \dfrac{1}{2} = \boxed{}$

How many $\dfrac{1}{3}$'s in 1?

$1 \div \dfrac{1}{3} = \boxed{}$

How many $\dfrac{1}{3}$'s in 3?

$3 \div \dfrac{1}{3} = \boxed{}$

How many $\dfrac{2}{3}$'s in 2?

$2 \div \dfrac{2}{3} = \boxed{}$

How many $\dfrac{1}{4}$'s in $\dfrac{1}{2}$?

$\dfrac{1}{2} \div \dfrac{1}{4} = \boxed{}$

How many $\dfrac{2}{5}$'s in $\dfrac{10}{5}$?

$\dfrac{10}{5} \div \dfrac{2}{5} = \boxed{}$

Ref: *Lab Sheet Annotations*, pages 160, 161 and 162.   ••••• H-54

Name _____ Date _____

Connect the names for the same number.

$\frac{1}{5}$	$\frac{6}{9}$
$\frac{2}{3}$	$\frac{3}{2}$
$1\frac{1}{2}$	$\frac{10}{12}$
$\frac{3}{4}$	$\frac{4}{20}$
$\frac{4}{5}$	$\frac{2}{10}$
$\frac{5}{6}$	$\frac{4}{6}$
$2\frac{1}{3}$	$\frac{8}{10}$
	$\frac{7}{3}$
	$\frac{6}{8}$
	$\frac{8}{6}$

Ref: *Lab Sheet Annotations*, pages 160 and 161.

● ● ● ● ● H-55

$\frac{33}{11} + \frac{4}{11} = 3\frac{4}{11}$ $\frac{3}{5} + \frac{2}{5} =$

$\frac{8}{8} + \frac{3}{8} = 1\frac{3}{8}$ $\frac{4}{2} + \frac{6}{3} =$

$\frac{10}{5} + \frac{2}{5} =$ Make up more problems like these.

$\frac{14}{7} + \frac{1}{7} =$

$\frac{14}{2} + \frac{1}{2} =$

$\frac{30}{5} + \frac{4}{5} =$

$\frac{5}{5} + \frac{6}{6} =$

$\frac{2}{2} + \frac{3}{3} + \frac{4}{4} =$

$\frac{8}{2} + \frac{3}{3} =$

Ref: *Lab Sheet Annotations*, page 160.   ● ● ● ● ● H-56

Name _____ Date _____

How many 8's are there in 32?

Make a quick guess and write it → ☐ ☐
                                        Guess   Answer

Look at this rod picture

to help you find the correct

answer.

$8 \overline{)32}$

There are ☐ eights

in 32.

Write in your guesses for all

the problems. Check them with your rods.

Guess Answer	Guess Answer
☐ ☐	☐ ☐
$9 \overline{)45}$	$7 \overline{)35}$
Guess Answer	Guess Answer
☐ ☐	☐ ☐
$8 \overline{)40}$	$3 \overline{)27}$
Guess Answer	Guess Answer
☐ ☐	☐ ☐
$8 \overline{)80}$	$6 \overline{)48}$

Ref: *Lab Sheet Annotations*, page 181.

Name _____ Date _____

Guess □ Answer □ $5\,\overline{)\,25}$	Guess □ Answer □ $4\,\overline{)\,36}$	Guess □ Answer □ $3\,\overline{)\,33}$
Guess □ Answer □ $8\,\overline{)\,56}$	Guess □ Answer □ $7\,\overline{)\,63}$	Guess □ Answer □ $6\,\overline{)\,54}$
Guess □ Answer □ $5\,\overline{)\,60}$	Guess □ Answer □ $16\,\overline{)\,64}$	Guess □ Answer □ $7\,\overline{)\,28}$
Guess □ Answer □ $8\,\overline{)\,96}$	Guess □ Answer □ $3\,\overline{)\,39}$	Guess □ Answer □ $9\,\overline{)\,108}$
Guess □ Answer □ $8\,\overline{)\,48}$	Guess □ Answer □ $9\,\overline{)\,81}$	Guess □ Answer □ $9\,\overline{)\,75}$

Ref: *Lab Sheet Annotations*, page 181.

●●●●● J-20

16 —— ÷ 4 ——→ ⬡ —— × 4 ——→ ☐

16 —— ÷ 2 ——→ ⬡ —— × 2 ——→ ☐

16 —— ÷ 8 ——→ ⬡ —— × 8 ——→ ☐

16 —— ÷ 1 ——→ ⬡ —— × 1 ——→ ☐

32 —— ÷ 32 ——→ ⬡ —— × 32 ——→ ☐

32 —— ÷ 4 ——→ ⬡ —— × 4 ——→ ☐

32 —— ÷ 8 ——→ ⬡ —— × 8 ——→ ☐

48 —— ÷ 8 ——→ ⬡ —— × 8 ——→ ☐

48 —— ÷ 6 ——→ ⬡ —— × 6 ——→ ☐

$$5\overline{)50}^{\,10} \qquad 7\overline{)70} \qquad 8\overline{)80} \qquad 9\overline{)90}$$

$$\frac{60}{6} = \boxed{10} \qquad\qquad \frac{40}{4} = \boxed{} \qquad\qquad \frac{20}{2} = \boxed{}$$

$$160 \div 16 = \boxed{10} \qquad 400 \div 40 = \boxed{} \qquad 720 \div 72 = \boxed{}$$

$$8\overline{)80} \qquad 8\overline{)16}$$

$$8\overline{)80+16}^{\,10+2}$$

$$8\overline{)96}$$

$$12\overline{)120} \qquad 12\overline{)24}$$

$$12\overline{)120+24}$$

$$12\overline{)144}$$

$$9\overline{)90} \qquad 9\overline{)90} \qquad 9\overline{)90} \qquad 9\overline{)27}$$

$$9\overline{)90+90+90+27}$$

$$9\overline{)270+27}$$

$$9\overline{)297}$$

Ref: *Lab Sheet Annotations*, page 182.

Name _____ Date _____

Change $3\overline{)45}$ to $3\overline{)\underset{30+\langle\!\langle 15\rangle\!\rangle}{\overset{10+\ 5\ =}{}}}$ ◯

Change $4\overline{)52}$ to $4\overline{)\underset{40+\langle\!\langle 12\rangle\!\rangle}{\overset{+\ \ \ =}{}}}$ ◯

Change $5\overline{)75}$ to $5\overline{)\underset{50+\langle\ \ \ \rangle}{\overset{+\ \ \ =}{}}}$ ◯

Change $6\overline{)78}$ to $6\overline{)\underset{\langle\ \ \ \rangle+18}{\overset{+\ \ \ =}{}}}$ ◯

Change $7\overline{)91}$ to $7\overline{)\underset{\langle\ \ \ \rangle+21}{\overset{+\ \ \ =}{}}}$ ◯

Change $8\overline{)104}$ to $8\overline{)\underset{80+\langle\ \ \ \rangle}{\overset{+\ \ \ =}{}}}$ ◯

Change $9\overline{)135}$ to $9\overline{)\underset{\langle\ \ \ \rangle+45}{\overset{+\ \ \ =}{}}}$ ◯

$$\frac{64}{4} = \frac{40}{4} + \frac{\ }{4} = \bigcirc$$

$$\frac{84}{7} = \frac{\ }{7} + \frac{14}{7} = \bigcirc$$

$$\frac{180}{10} = \frac{100}{10} + \frac{\ }{10} = \bigcirc$$

Ref: Lab Sheet Annotations, page 182.

•••••• J-23

Name _____   Date _____

Change $3\overline{)72}$ to $3\overline{)30 + 30 + ⬡12}$ $\dfrac{10 + 10 + 4}{} = \bigcirc$

Change $3\overline{)72}$ to $3\overline{)⬡ + 12}$ $= \bigcirc$

Change $5\overline{)160}$ to $5\overline{)⬡ + 10}$ $= \bigcirc$

Change $6\overline{)132}$ to $6\overline{)⬡ + \square}$ $\dfrac{20 \quad\quad 2}{} = \bigcirc$

Change $7\overline{)245}$ to $7\overline{)⬡ + \square}$ $\dfrac{30 \quad\quad 5}{} = \bigcirc$

Change $8\overline{)368}$ to $8\overline{)⬡ + \square}$ $\dfrac{40 \quad\quad 6}{} = \bigcirc$

Change $9\overline{)288}$ to $9\overline{)⬡ + 18}$ $= \bigcirc$

$\dfrac{185}{5} = \dfrac{150}{5} + \dfrac{\square}{5} = \bigcirc$ $\dfrac{96}{4} = \dfrac{\square}{\bigcirc} + \dfrac{16}{4} = \bigcirc$

$\dfrac{75}{3} = \dfrac{\square}{\bigcirc} + \dfrac{15}{3} = \bigcirc$ $\dfrac{105}{3} = \dfrac{\square}{3} + \dfrac{15}{3} = \bigcirc$

$96 \div 6 = (60 \div 6) + (\square \div 6) = \bigcirc$

Ref: *Lab Sheet Annotations*, page 182.

••••• J-24

Page 4

$$\frac{85}{5} = \frac{50}{5} + \frac{35}{5} = \bigcirc \qquad \bigcirc$$

$$\frac{91}{7} = \frac{\square}{7} + \frac{21}{7} = \bigcirc$$

$$\frac{63}{3} = \frac{30}{3} + \frac{\square}{3} + \frac{3}{3} = \bigcirc$$

$$\frac{92}{4} = \frac{\square}{4} + \frac{\square}{4} + \frac{12}{4} = \bigcirc$$

$$\frac{72}{4} = \frac{40}{4} + \frac{\square}{4} = \bigcirc$$

$$\frac{189}{7} = \frac{70}{7} + \frac{\square}{7} + \frac{49}{7} = \bigcirc$$

$$\frac{42}{12} = \frac{\square}{12} + \frac{12}{12} + \frac{12}{12} + \frac{6}{12} = \bigcirc$$

fold here

Page 1

Name : _____

Date : _____

$3\overline{)12}$ $4\overline{)12}$ $6\overline{)12}$

$5\overline{)10}$ $1\overline{)10}$ $10\overline{)10}$

$10\overline{)50}$ $3\overline{)15}$ $8\overline{)24}$

$7\overline{)21}$ $6\overline{)36}$ $20\overline{)100}$

$3\overline{)33}$ $4\overline{)32}$ $12\overline{)36}$

$8\overline{)16}$ $8\overline{)40}$ $8\overline{)4}$

	true	false
$8 \div 2 > 8 - 2$	T	F
$18 \div 3 = \dfrac{18}{3}$	T	F
$(5 \times 5) - 5 = 5$	T	F
$3\overline{)6}^{\,\frac{2}{}}$	T	F
$6\overline{)3}^{\,\frac{2}{}}$	T	F
$5\overline{)20}, \quad \dfrac{16}{4}, \quad 36 \div 9$ are all names for the number four.	T	F
$(75 - 3) + 50 \neq 75$	T	F
$\dfrac{60}{6} + \dfrac{48}{6} = 18$	T	F
$\dfrac{8}{8} + \dfrac{7}{7} + \dfrac{6}{6} + \dfrac{5}{5} = \dfrac{26}{26}$	T	F

Page 3

- -

fold here

$66 - 11 = \square$

$\dfrac{66}{11} = \square$

$3\overline{)27}$

$6\overline{)42}$

$7\overline{)6}^{\,6}$

$\dfrac{1}{3}$ of $9 = \bigcirc$

$\dfrac{9}{3} = \bigcirc$

$28 \div \square = 4$

$\dfrac{1}{4}$ of $28 = \square$

$100 \div 5 = \square$

$100 - 20 = \square$

$60 \div 30 = \square$

$60 \div 3 = \square$

$81 \div 9 = 10 - \square$

Page 2

Name _____ Date _____

three times fifteen - - - - - - - - - - - - $\begin{array}{r} 100 \\ \times\ 10 \\ \hline 1000 \end{array}$

one half of thirty $\frac{4}{5} \times 25$

thirty divided by two $9\overline{)180}$

ten times one hundred - - - - - - - - - $88 \div 11$

How many fives in seventy-five? $30 \div 2$

three plus fifteen $7 + \square$

seven plus some number 3×15

How many fifties in one thousand? $5\overline{)75}$

some number times itself equals another number $\frac{1}{2} \times 30$

one-hundred eighty divided by nine $\square \times \square = \langle\ \rangle$

four fifths of twenty-five $3 + 15$

eighty-eight divided by eleven $1,000 \div 50$

Ref: *Lab Sheet Annotations*, page 195.   ● ● ● ● ● K-17

Use $+$, $-$, $\times$,and $(\ )$ to make these

sentences true.

2 3 4 = 9	3 2 1 = 6
2 3 4 = 1	3 2 1 = ☐
2 3 4 = 10	3 2 1 = ☐
$(2 + 3) \times 4 = 20$	3 2 1 = ☐
2 3 4 = 14	3 2 1 = ☐
2 3 4 = 24	3 2 1 = ☐
	3 2 1 = ☐
3 3 3 = 9	3 2 1 = ☐
3 3 3 = 3	3 2 1 = ☐
3 3 3 = 6	3 2 1 = ☐
3 3 3 = 12	3 2 1 = ☐
	3 2 1 = ☐

Ref: *Lab Sheet Annotations*, page 196.

• • • • • • K-18

Use these symbols

to make true

sentences.

4	3	2	1	=	11
4	3	2	1	=	10
4	3	2	1	=	9
4	3	2	1	=	8
4	3	2	1	=	7
4	3	2	1	=	6
4	3	2	1	=	5
4	3	2	1	=	4
4	3	2	1	=	3
4	3	2	1	=	2
4	3	2	1	=	1
4	3	2	1	=	0
4	3	2	1	=	15
4	3	2	1	=	24

Ref: *Lab Sheet Annotations*, page 196.

• • • • • K-19

Name _____ Date _____

Draw lines from the equation to the
rule describing it.

$60 \div 60 = 1$

$\square \times \triangle = \triangle \times \square$

$0 \times 9 = 9 \times 0$

$4 \div 1 = 4 \times 1$

$1 \div 1 = 1$

$\frac{1}{2} \div 1 = \frac{1}{2}$

$\square \div \square = 1$

$600 + 0 = 600$

$4 + 7 = 7 + 4$

$8 \div 1 = 8$

$34 \div 2 = 17$

$\square \div 1 = \square$

$4 \times 7 = 7 \times 4$

$77 \times 77 = 77 \times 77$

Ref: *Lab Sheet Annotations*, pages 186 and 197.

Name _____ Date _____

Cross-Number

Puzzle

Across		
a.	212 double
d.	60 x 2
f.	9 x 3
g.	The number of cents in 3 dimes + 3 pennies
i.	(4 x 10) + (2 + 3)
l.	The number of days in 2 weeks plus 1 day
n.	3^2 x 5
o.	25 – 7
q.	10 x 10 x 10
s.	3 x 3 x 3
t.	$(\frac{1}{2}$ x 60) + $(\frac{1}{2}$ x 12)
u.	The number of fingers on one hand
v.	$\frac{1}{4}$ x 20

Down		
b.	The number of cents in 4 nickles + 2 pennies
c.	49 minus 2
d.	six plus seven
e.	2 x 10 + 3
h.	The number of cents in 2 quarters + 1 penny
i.	11 x 4
j.	5 tens plus 5 ones
k.	3 + 3 + 3 + 3 + 3 + 3
m.	The number of cents in 1 quarter + 3 dimes + 3 pennies
o.	The number of things in one dozen
p.	$10^2 + 5^2$
r.	The number of days in a year

●●●●● K-21

Name _____ Date _____

Dear ___

Please correct my paper. I made <u>some</u> mistakes.

Love,

$5 \times 5 = 25$

$$\begin{array}{r} 200 \\ -65 \\ \hline 145 \end{array}$$

$$\begin{array}{r} 6 \\ 6 \\ 6 \\ +\ 6 \\ \hline 2 \times 12 \end{array}$$

$$\begin{array}{r} 14 \\ 26 \\ 31 \\ +165 \\ \hline 238 \end{array}$$

$4 + 5 + 6 = 14$

$6 \times 6 = 30$

$2 \times 16 = 32$

$$\begin{array}{r} 29 \\ 30 \\ +\ 31 \\ \hline 80 \end{array}$$

$$\begin{array}{r} 30 \\ 31 \\ +\ 32 \\ \hline 93 \end{array}$$

$2 \times 3 \times 3 < 18$

$$\begin{array}{r} 716 \\ -615 \\ \hline 11 \end{array}$$

$$\begin{array}{r} 834 \\ -320 \\ \hline 514 \end{array}$$

100 minutes = one hour

$3 > 4$

$\dfrac{3}{4} = \dfrac{6}{8}$

3 x 2
4 x 5
8 x 4
5 x 3   ┌─────────┐
7 x 1   │   │
6 x 6   │ <25   │
2 x 9   │   │
9 x 3   └─────────┘
4 x 4
6 x 3
0 x 9

3 x 2
4 x 5
8 x 4
5 x 3   ┌──────────┐
7 x 1   │ is a   │
6 x 6   │ square │
2 x 9   └──────────┘
9 x 3
4 x 4
6 x 3
0 x 9

3 x 2
4 x 5
8 x 4
5 x 3   ┌──────────┐
7 x 1   │ is an   │
6 x 6   │ even   │
2 x 9   │ number │
9 x 3   └──────────┘
4 x 4
6 x 3
0 x 9

3 x 2 = □
4 x 5 = □
8 x 4 = □
5 x 3 = □
7 x 1 = □
6 x 6 = □
2 x 9 = □
9 x 3 = □
4 x 4 = □
6 x 3 = □
0 x 9 = □

Ref: *Lab Sheet Annotations*, page 206.   • • • • • • L-17

Top-left quadrant:

3 x 3
5 x 3
6 x 4
9 x 9
7 x 6
8 x 7 - - - - >50
6 x 3
9 x 7
8 x 8
5 x 7
7 x 7

Top-right quadrant:

3 x 3 - - - -
5 x 3
6 x 4
9 x 9
7 x 6   is a
8 x 7   square
6 x 3
9 x 7
8 x 8
5 x 7
7 x 7

Bottom-left quadrant:

3 x 3
5 x 3
6 x 4
9 x 9 - - - -
7 x 6   is an
8 x 7   odd number
6 x 3
9 x 7
8 x 8
5 x 7
7 x 7

Bottom-right quadrant:

3 x 3 = [?]
5 x 3 = [ ]
6 x 4 = [ ]
9 x 9 = [ ]
7 x 6 = [ ]
8 x 7 = [ ]
6 x 3 = [ ]
9 x 7 = [ ]
8 x 8 = [ ]
5 x 7 = [ ]
7 x 7 = [ ]

Ref: *Lab Sheet Annotations*, page 206.

● ● ● ● ● L-18

Use >, =, < to make these sentences true.

MATCH

40 pennies	20 nickels
5 nickels	25 cents
½ dollar	1 cent
3 dimes	4 dimes
4 quarters	3 nickels
15 cents	$1\frac{1}{2}$ dimes
¼ dollar	2 quarters
2 nickels	$\frac{1}{10}$ dollar
100 pennies	1 nickel + 1 quarter
	8 nickels

1 nickel	⌵	10 cents
1 quarter		5 nickels
1 dime		10 cents
1 nickel		5 cents
1 dime		1 nickel
5 dimes		1 quarter
50 cents		2 quarters
1 quarter		6 nickels
1 dollar		100 cents
10 dimes		1 dollar
2 nickels		3 dimes
4 quarter		1 dollar

Ref: *Lab Sheet Annotations*, page 207.

Name _____ Date _____

<table>
<tr><td colspan="2">Make <u>false sentences</u> by finishing the following problems.</td><td colspan="2">Make <u>true sentences</u> by finishing the following problems.</td></tr>
</table>

$9 = 5 + \boxed{}$

$17 > \boxed{}$

$833 \neq \boxed{}$

$5 \times 5 \leq \boxed{}$

$$\begin{array}{r} 99 \\ +101 \\ \hline \end{array} \qquad \begin{array}{r} 101 \\ -99 \\ \hline \end{array}$$

$$\begin{array}{r} 6000 \\ -5999 \\ \hline \end{array}$$

$9 = 5 + \boxed{}$

$17 > \boxed{}$

$833 \neq \boxed{}$

$5 \times 5 \leq \boxed{}$

$$\begin{array}{r} 99 \\ +101 \\ \hline \end{array} \qquad \begin{array}{r} 101 \\ -99 \\ \hline \end{array}$$

$$\begin{array}{r} 6000 \\ -5999 \\ \hline \end{array}$$

Ref: *Lab Sheet Annotations*, page 207.

●●●●● L-20

7019

Seven hundred nineteen

7190

Seven thousand nineteen

719

Seven thousand one hundred nine

70019

Seven thousand one hundred ninety

7109

Seventy thousand nineteen

70190

Seventy thousand one hundred nine

71090

Seventy thousand one hundred ninety

70109

Seventy-one thousand nine

71900

Seventy-one thousand ninety

71009

Seventy-one thousand nine hundred

Ref: *Lab Sheet Annotations*, page 218.

Name _____ Date _____

What is the smallest number and the largest

number you can make with the following digits?

Smallest Number	Digits	Largest Number
	3,7	
	4,2,9	
	7,8,3	
	2,6,2	
	4,2,8;3	
	9,9,2,8	
	0,3,1,7	
	0,3,0,0	
	4,9,2,0	
	3,6,4,0,1,3	

Ref: *Lab Sheet Annotations*, page 218.

What is the smallest number and the largest
number you can make with the following digits?

Smallest	Digits	Largest
	6,5,8	
	4,0,9	
	3,3,1,3	
	3,2,1,4	
	1,2,3,4,0	

Digits	Write all the possible numbers these digits can make.					
4,2,5	425	452	254			
3,2,3						
6,0,9						
4,7,8						
5,5,5						

Ref: *Lab Sheet Annotations*, page 218.   ●●●●● M-19

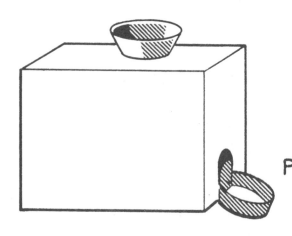

The Penny Machine

Pennies

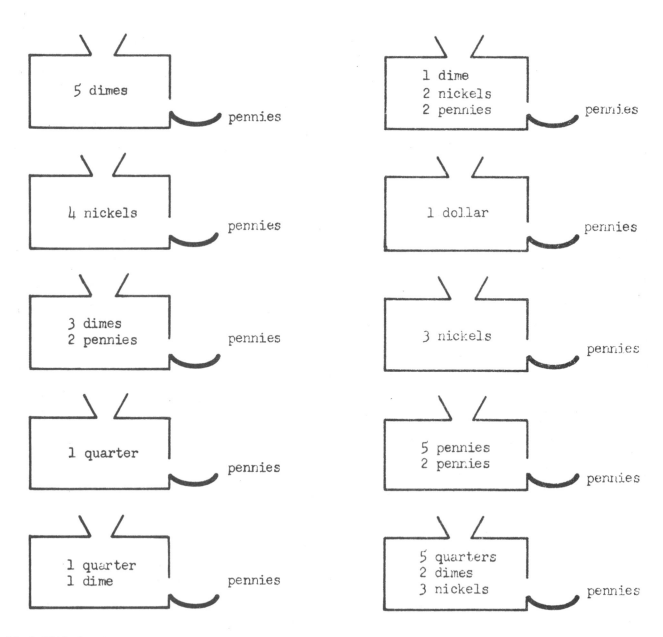

5 dimes ____ pennies

1 dime
2 nickels
2 pennies ____ pennies

4 nickels ____ pennies

1 dollar ____ pennies

3 dimes
2 pennies ____ pennies

3 nickels ____ pennies

1 quarter ____ pennies

5 pennies
2 pennies ____ pennies

1 quarter
1 dime ____ pennies

5 quarters
2 dimes
3 nickels ____ pennies

Ref: *Lab Sheet Annotations*, page 220.

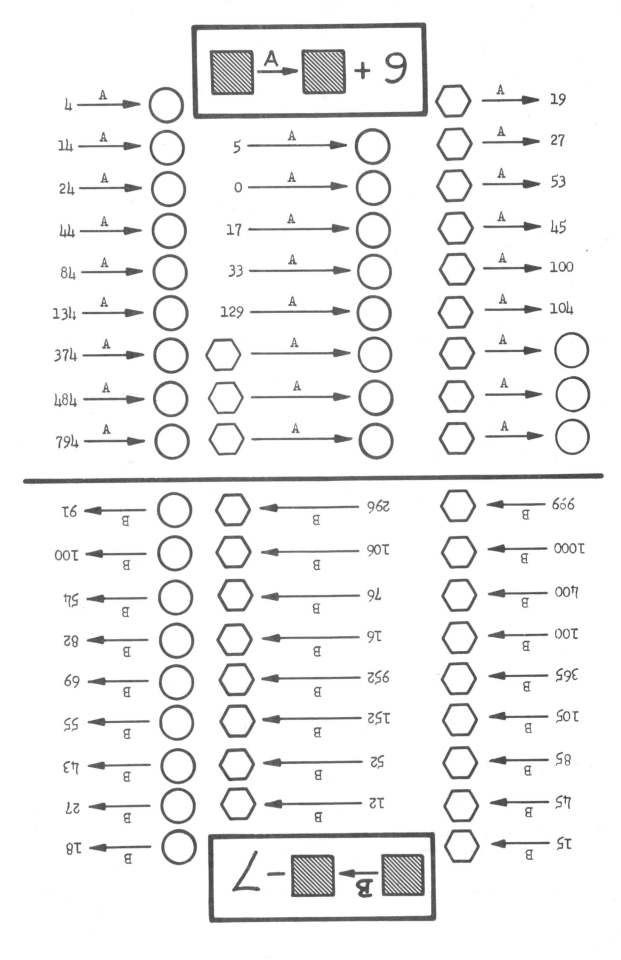

Ref: *Lab Sheet Annotations*, page 236.

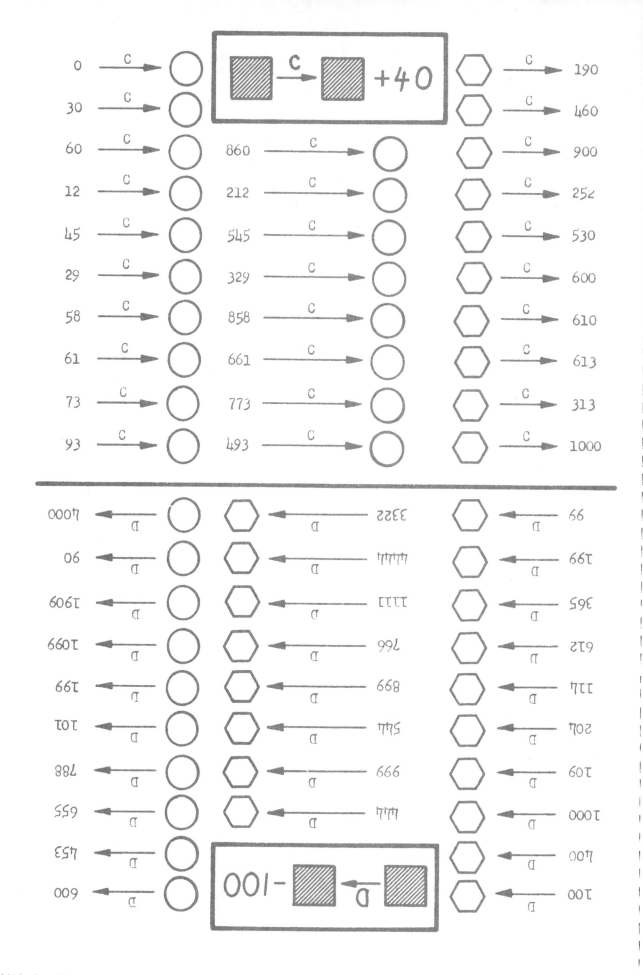

Ref: *Lab Sheet Annotations,* page 236.

Name

Date

$$\square \xrightarrow{E} \square \quad +37$$

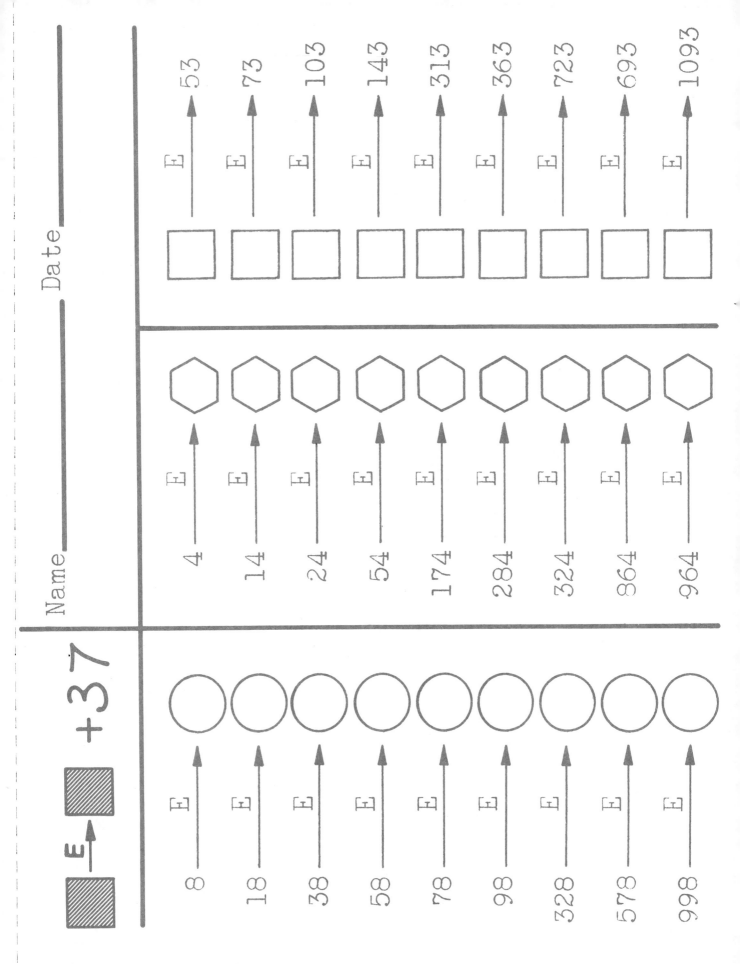

53	73	103	143	313	363	723	693	1093
E	E	E	E	E	E	E	E	E
□	□	□	□	□	□	□	□	□

⬡	⬡	⬡	⬡	⬡	⬡	⬡	⬡	⬡
E	E	E	E	E	E	E	E	E
4	14	24	54	174	284	324	864	964

○	○	○	○	○	○	○	○	○
E	E	E	E	E	E	E	E	E
8	18	38	58	78	98	328	578	998

Ref: *Lab Sheet Annotations*, page 236.

●●●●● N-13

Name

Date

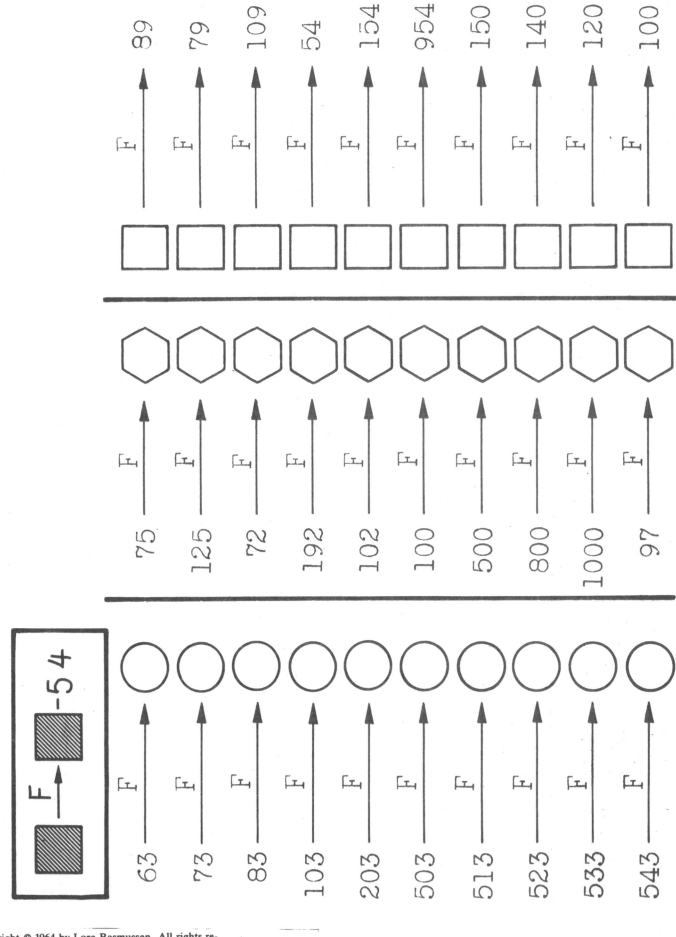

Ref: *Lab Sheet Annotations*, page 236.

●●●●● N-14

Name _____

Date _____

Write in the rules that we are using.

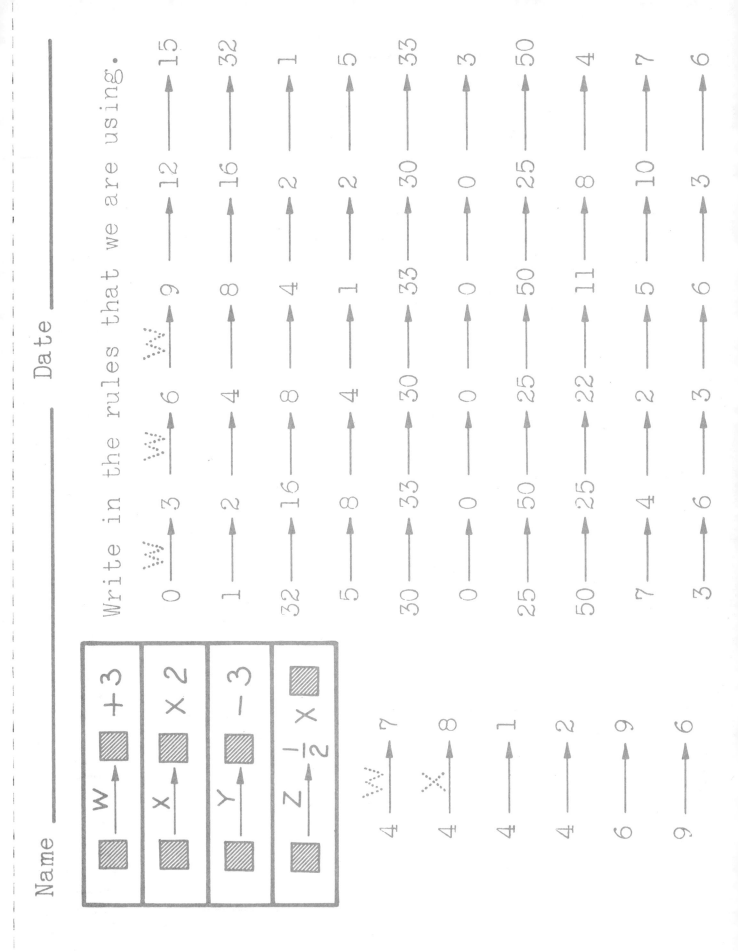

Ref: *Lab Sheet Annotations*, page 237.

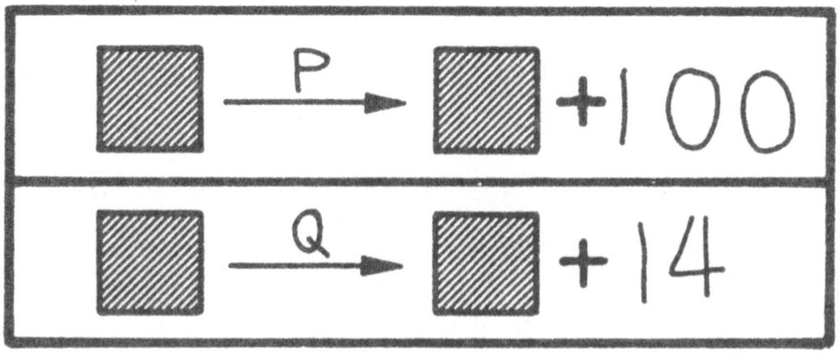

□ — P → □	+100	
□ — Q → □	+14	

4 — QP → (hexagon)

4 — PQ → (circle)

12 — QP → (hexagon)

12 — PQ → (circle)

90 — Q → (hexagon)

90 — QP → (circle)

25 — Q → (hexagon)

25 — QP → (circle)

125 — P → (hexagon)

125 — PQ → (circle)

125 — QP → (hexagon)

7 — PP → (circle)

0 — QQ → (hexagon)

0 — PPP → (circle)

0 — PPQQ → (hexagon)

1 — PQP → (circle)

1 — QPP → (hexagon)

1 — PPQ → (circle)

1 — QQP → (hexagon)

307 — PQ → (circle)

307 — QP → (hexagon)

529 — PPPPQ → (circle)

Ref: *Lab Sheet Annotations*, page 238.

•••••• N-16

Here is a graph for the rule: 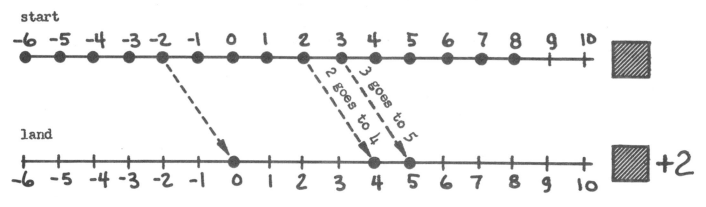 +2
Can you finish it?

Below are two more graphs to finish.

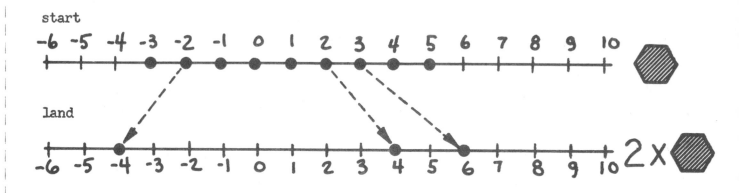

Ref: *Lab Sheet Annotations*, page 238.

•••••• N-17

Name _____ Date _____

Look at the graphs.

Then finish writing

the rules for them.

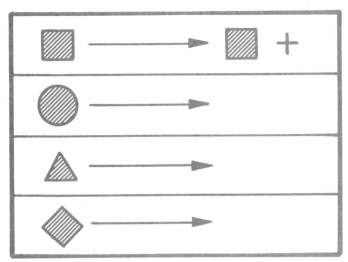

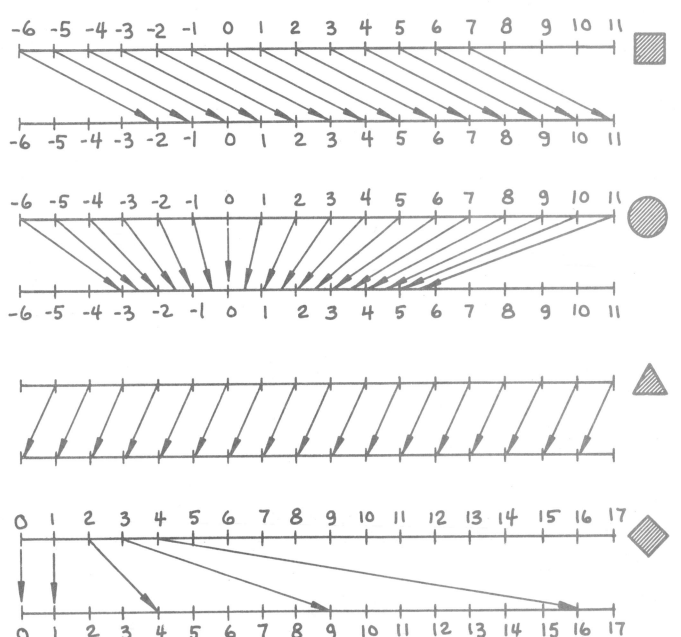

Ref: *Lab Sheet Annotations*, page 239.

••••• N-18

Name _____ Date _____

<u>Prime</u> <u>Number</u> <u>Sieve</u>

This lab sheet goes with lab sheet 0-9. Get 0-9.

② is the first light number on the number chain. Darken every <u>second</u>

number <u>after</u> 2:

③ is the next light number. Darken every <u>third</u> number <u>after</u> 3:

Now the beginning of the number chain looks like this:

⑤ is the next light number. Darken every <u>fifth</u> number <u>after</u> 5. The

next light number is ⑦ . Darken every <u>seventh</u> number <u>after</u> 7.

Now make a list of all the light numbers that are left on the number chain.
These are all of the <u>prime numbers</u> from 1 to 100.

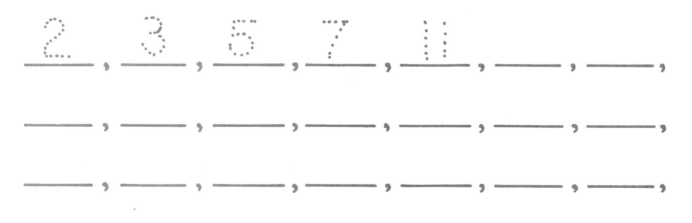

Now work on lab sheet 0-8.

Ref: *Lab Sheet Annotations*, page 244.

Name _____ Date _____

Put in these two-story factor houses the prime numbers under 50 and their

factor families.

Check again and make sure that the numbers you wrote about have <u>no</u> <u>other</u>

<u>factors.</u>

●●●●● 0-8

Name_____ Date_____

Sheet O-7 tells you what to do.

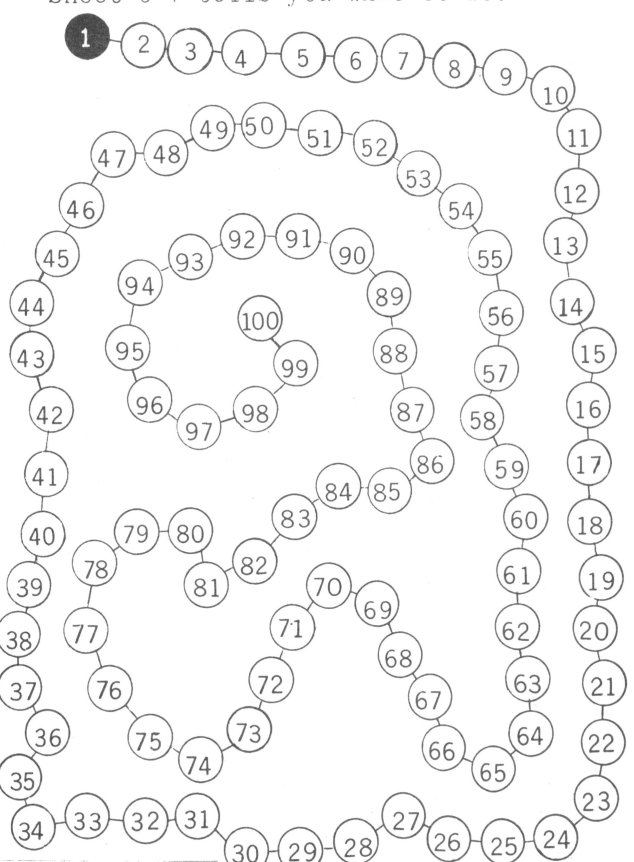

Ref: *Lab Sheet Annotations*, page 244.

• • • • • •O-9

$68 = 2 \times \square$

$\square = 2 \times \bigcirc$

$68 = 2 \times 2 \times \bigcirc$

The prime factors of 68 are: 2, 2, and $\bigcirc$.

$36 = 2 \times \square$

$\square = 2 \times \bigcirc$

$\bigcirc = 3 \times \triangle$

$36 = 2 \times 2 \times 3 \times \triangle$

The prime factors of 36 are: _____ , _____ , _____ , and $\triangle$.

$70 = 2 \times \square$

$\square = 5 \times \triangle$

$70 = 2 \times 5 \times \triangle$

The prime factors of 70 are _____ , _____ , and $\triangle$.

$2, 2, 2, 5$ are the prime factors of $\bigcirc$

$2 \times 2 \times 2 \times 5 = \bigcirc$

$3, 7$ are the prime factors of $= \square$

$3 \times 7 = \square$

$5, 5, 2$ are the prime factors of $\bigcirc$.

$5, 5, 3$ are the prime factors of $\triangle$.

$5, 3, 3$ are the prime factors of $\boxed{}$.

$5, 5, 2, 2$ are the prime factors of $\square$.

Ref: *Lab Sheet Annotations*, page 245.

●●●●● 0-10

Name _____ Date _____

Circle all the prime numbers you see below:

15

3 5

9 4

13 6

19 2

16 8 11 7

22 23 31 10 27

Write down the prime factors of:

12 ___(2, 2, 3)_____

16 ___(   )_____

18 _____

26 _____

30 _____

44 _____

27 _____

46 _____

42 _____

49 _____

Ref: *Lab Sheet Annotations*, page 245.

Name _____ Date _____

Here are numbers and their prime factor products.

$14 = 2 \times 7$

$9 = 3 \times 3$

$51 = 3 \times 17$

$24 = 2 \times 2 \times 2 \times 3$

Remember, in $8 = \boxed{2} \times \boxed{2} \times \boxed{2}$

you must write the same number in

all the $\boxed{}$'s

___

You do these prime factor problems:

$15 = \bigcirc \times \square$

$30 = \bigcirc \times \square \times \triangle$

$45 = \boxed{3} \times \boxed{3} \times \square$

$60 = \square \times \square \times \boxed{5} \times \triangle$

$40 = \square \times \square \times \square \times \triangle$

$25 = \bigcirc \times \bigcirc$

$55 = \square \times \bigcirc$

$28 = \bigcirc \times \bigcirc \times \square$

$36 = \square \times \square \times \triangle \times \triangle$

$32 = \square \times \square \times \square \times \square \quad \square$

$81 = \underline{} \times \underline{} \times \underline{} \times \underline{}$

$18 =$

$39 =$

$49 =$

The BIG CUBE weighs ☐ marbles.

The LITTLE CUBE weighs ☐ marbles.

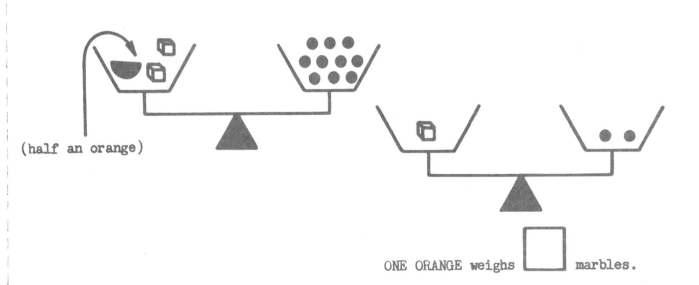

(half an orange)

ONE ORANGE weighs ☐ marbles.

Ref: *Lab Sheet Annotations*, page 256.

Name _____ Date _____

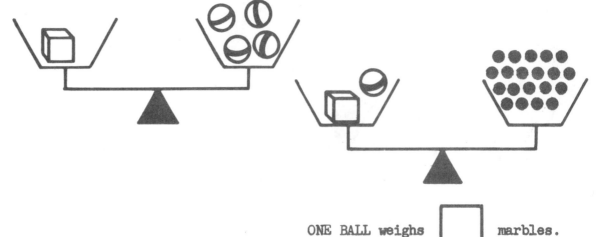

ONE BALL weighs ⬜ marbles.

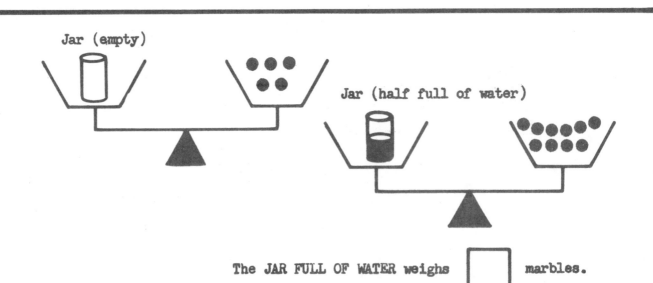

ONE BALL weighs ⬜ marbles.

Jar (empty)

Jar (half full of water)

The JAR FULL OF WATER weighs ⬜ marbles.

Ref: *Lab Sheet Annotations*, page 256.

Name _____ Date _____

ONE CUBE weighs [ ] marbles.

Jar (empty)   Jar (full of water)

A HALF FULL JAR OF WATER

weighs [ ] marbles.

ONE BLACK CUBE weighs [ ] marbles.

THE BALL weighs [ ] marbles.

Ref: *Lab Sheet Annotations*, page 256.

1

A

3
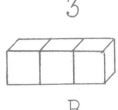
B

4
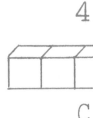
C

A + B + C = ◯

A ✗ B ✗ C = △

---

4   6   2

D   E   F

D + E + F = ◯

D ✗ E ✗ F = △

9   2   2

G   H   I

G + H + I = ◯

G ✗ H ✗ I = △

    △   ◯

K   L   M

K + L + M = 9

K ✗ L ✗ M = 24

three numbers

 + △ + ◯ = 6

 ✗ △ ✗ ◯ = 6

Ref: *Lab Sheet Annotations*, page 256.

Name _____ Date _____

WHAT RODS ARE
UNDER THE CUP?

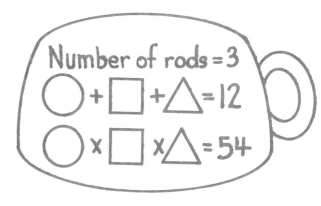

Number of rods = 3

$\bigcirc + \square + \triangle = 12$

$\bigcirc \times \square \times \triangle = 54$

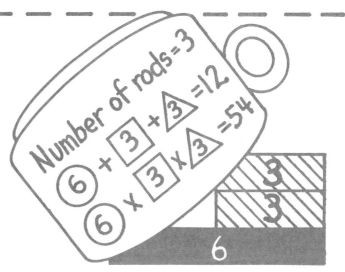

Number of rods = 3

$6 + \boxed{3} + \boxed{3} = 12$

$6 \times \boxed{3} \times \boxed{3} = 54$

3
3
6

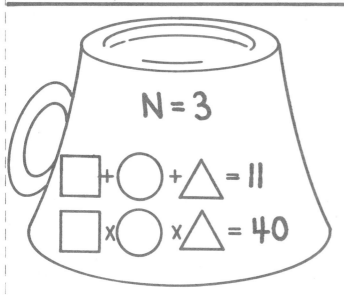

N = 3

$\square + \bigcirc + \triangle = 11$

$\square \times \bigcirc \times \triangle = 40$

Check your answer
with your rods.

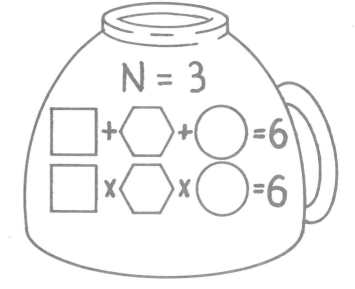

N = 3

$\square + \hexagon + \bigcirc = 6$

$\square \times \hexagon \times \bigcirc = 6$

Check your answer
with your rods.

Ref: *Lab Sheet Annotations*, page 258.

Name _____ Date _____

WHAT RODS ARE UNDER THE CUP ?

N=3

□ + ○ + △ = 6

□ × ○ × △ = 8

N=2

□ + ○ = 2

□ × ○ = 1

N=3

□ + ○ + ⬡ = 3

□ × ○ × ⬡ = 1

N=2

⬡ + ○ = 12

⬡ × ○ = 32

Ref: *Lab Sheet Annotations*, page 258.

BLOCKS AND CUPS: I have 15 blocks and a large stack of cups. There are many ways in which I can arrange my 15 blocks in the cups. I could put 3 blocks in each of 5 cups like this:

Fill in the ◯'s and ☐'s below to show some of the other ways I can arrange my 15 blocks.

****

3 cups; ☐ blocks in each cup

◯ cups; 15 blocks in each cup

◯ cups; ☐ blocks in each cup

◯ cups; ☐ blocks in each cup

2 cups; 10 blocks in one cup
         ☐ blocks in the other cup

2 cups;   5 blocks in one cup

         $(15 - ☐)$ blocks in the other cup

NOW GO ON TO THE BACK.

Ref: *Lab Sheet Annotations*, page 260. ●●●●● Q-7

Name _____ Date _____

ATTENTION! Do the other side of this sheet before you start on this side. THANK YOU!
****

REMEMBER, we have <u>exactly</u> 15 blocks to put into the cups. ************

2 cups;   7 blocks in one cup
          (4 × ☐) blocks in the other cup

3 cups;   3 blocks in one cup
          (3 + ☐) blocks in another cup
          (3 + ☐ + ☐) blocks in another cup

5 cups;   ☐ blocks in one cup
          (☐ + 1) blocks in another cup
          (☐ + 2) blocks in another cup
          (☐ + 3) blocks in another cup
          (☐ + 4) blocks in another cup

5 cups;   (☐ - 3) blocks in one cup
          (☐ - 2) blocks in another cup
          (☐ - 1) blocks in another cup
          ☐ blocks in another cup
          (☐ + 1) blocks in another cup

Ref: *Lab Sheet Annotations*, page 260.   ●●●●● Q-8

Could you make a
SQUARE with sides
the same lengths
as these lines?

YES   NO

_____
_____
_____

Could you make a
TRIANGLE with
sides the same
length as these
lines?
                YES   NO

_____
_____

Could you make a
SQUARE with sides
the same lengths
as these lines?

YES   NO

_____
_____
_____

Could you
make a
RECTANGLE
with sides
the same
lengths as
these lines?

YES   NO

Could you make a
TRIANGLE with
sides the same
lengths as these
lines?
                YES   NO

_____
_____
_____

NAME _____

DATE _____

Now DRAW these
SQUARES,
TRIANGLES, and
RECTANGLES
if you can.

Ref: *Lab Sheet Annotations*, page 288.

••••• S-9

How many rectangles
do you see in this
picture?

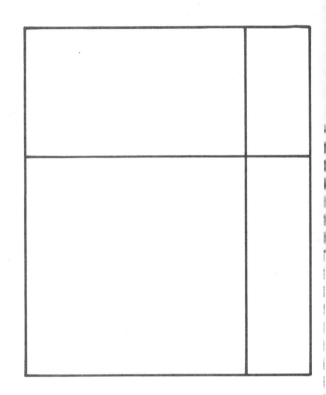

How many parallelograms
do you see in this
picture?

Ref: *Lab Sheet Annotations*, page 288.

●●●●● S-10

How many triangles do you see in this picture?

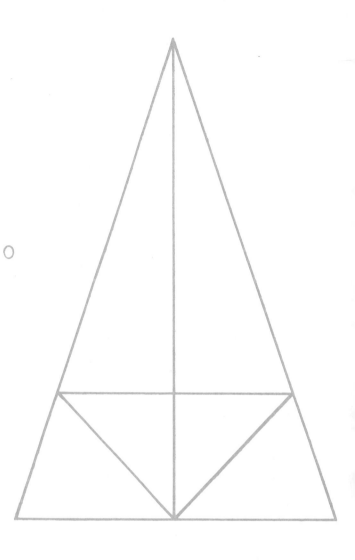

How many triangles do you see in this picture?

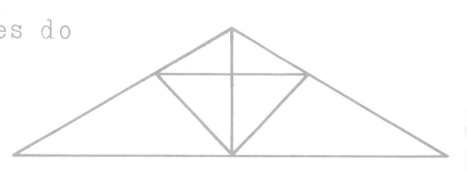

Ref: *Lab Sheet Annotations*, page 289.   ● ● ● ● ● S-11

Name _____ Date _____

RECTANGLES

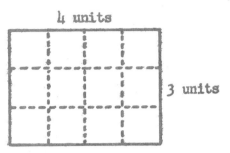

4 units

3 units

This rectangle is __4__ units long

and __3__ units wide.

Its border (the perimeter) is __14__ units long.

The perimeter = (3 + 4 + 3 + 4) units.

The amount of space inside the rectangle is called its area.

The area is __12__ square units.

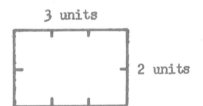

3 units

2 units

This rectangle is _____ units long

and _____ units wide.

Its perimeter (all around) is _____ units.

Its area is _____ square units.

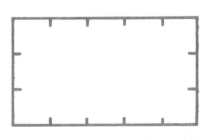

This rectangle is _____ units long

and _____ units wide.

Its perimeter is _____ units.

Its area is _____ square units.

Name _____ Date _____

Draw rectangles 1, 2, 3 and 4.
Then fill in the rest of the chart.

	Length	Width	Area	Perimeter
1	5 units	3 units	_____ sq. units	_____ units
2	2 units	8 units	_____ sq. units	_____ units
3	3 units	3 units	_____ sq. units	_____ units
4	4 units	2½ units	_____ sq. units	_____ units

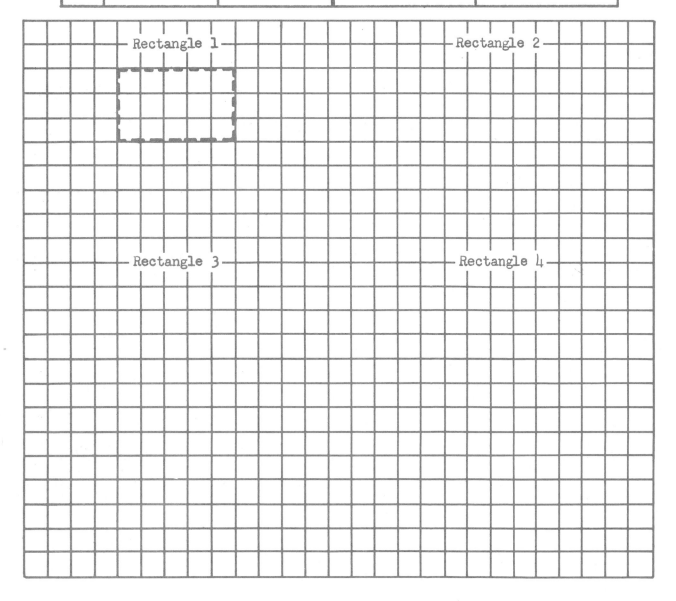

Rectangle 1   Rectangle 2

Rectangle 3   Rectangle 4

Ref: *Lab Sheet Annotations*, page 302.

Name _____ Date _____

Draw a rectangle that is 4 units wide and 5 units long.

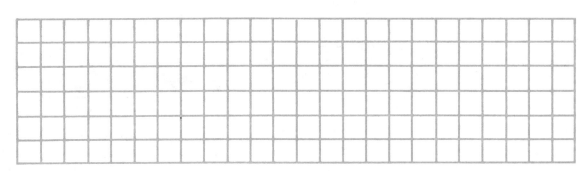

What is the area of your rectangle? _____ square units

What is its perimeter? _____ units

Draw a rectangle that is 8 units long and has an area of 16 square units.

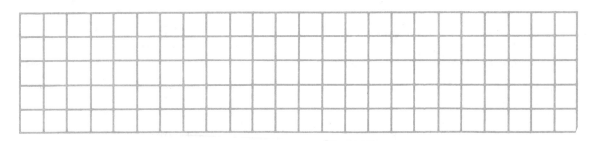

How wide is the rectangle? _____ units

What is its perimeter? _____ units

Draw a rectangle that is 12 units long and has a perimeter of 26 units.

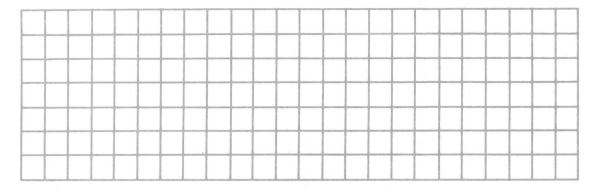

What is its width? _____ units

What is its area? _____ square units

Ref: *Lab Sheet Annotations*, page 302.

Name _____

Date _____

AREAS

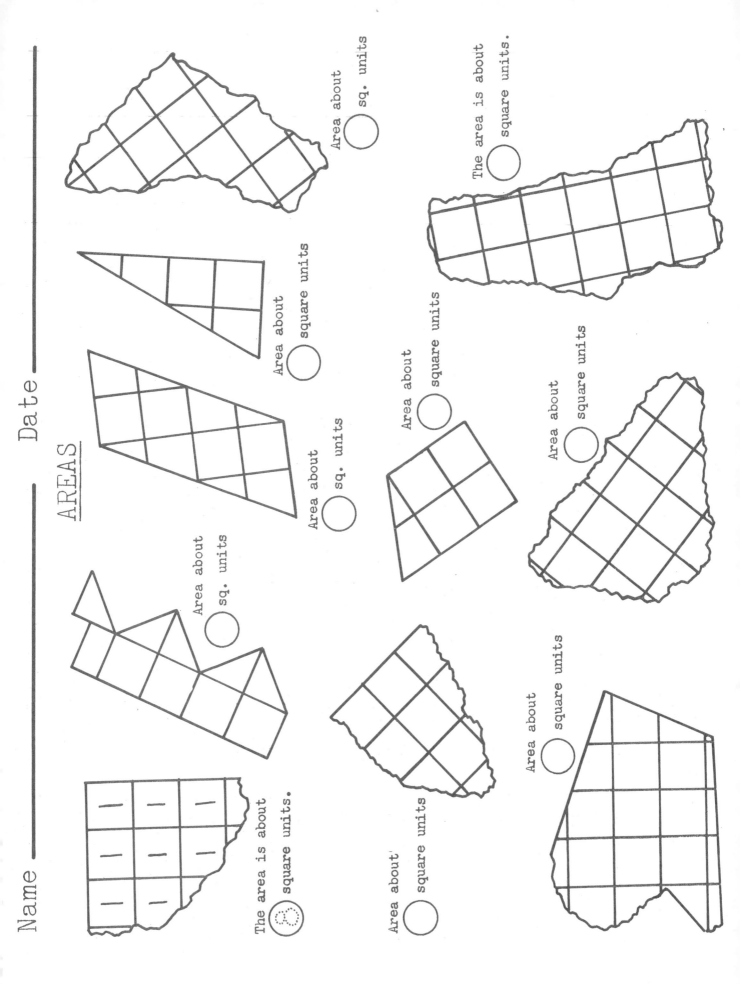

Area about ⬭ sq. units

The area is about ⬭ square units.

Area about ⬭ square units

Area about ⬭ square units

Area about ⬭ square units

Area about ⬭ sq. units

Area about ⬭ sq. units

Area about ⬭ square units

The area is about ⬭ square units.

Area about' ⬭ square units

Area about ⬭ square units

Ref: *Lab Sheet Annotations*, page 303.

●●●●●● T-24

Name _____ Date _____

Your white rod fits this picture. It is _____ cm long,

_____ cm wide, _____ cm high. It is made of

1 cubic centimeter of wood; 1 cm^3

1 cm^3

The _____ rod fits here. It is _____ cm long,

_____ cm wide, _____ cm high. It is made of _____ cubic

centimeters of wood; _____ cm^3

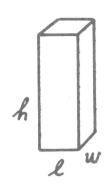

h

l w

This is a picture of the _____ rod.

l = _____ cm

w = _____ cm

h = _____ cm

In this building are

_____ cubic centimeters

of wood; _____ cm^3

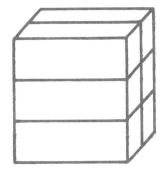

This is a picture of _____ green rods.

l = _____ cm

w = _____ cm

h = _____ cm

In this building are

_____ cubic centimeters

of wood; _____ cm^3

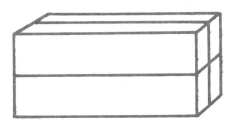

How many cubic centimeters of wood are in this rod

building?

We say: Its volume is _____ cubic centimeters.

_____ cm^3

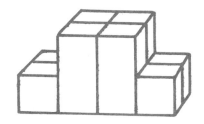

The volume of this rod building is _____ cm^3

Ref: *Lab Sheet Annotations*, page 304.

●●●●●●T-25

Build these models of buildings with your rods. Then answer the questions.

Church

Garage

Bank

Tower

Which building has the most cubic units of space in it?

The _____ has the most.

It has [ ] cubic units of space.

Which building needs the most ground to stand on?

The _____ needs the most.

It needs [ ] square units of ground.

Which building will take the longest to walk around?

The _____ and the _____ .

Both are [ ] units around.

Which building needs the least roofing?

It is the _____ .

It needs [ ] square units of roofing.

Which building needs the most paint? (Don't paint the roof.)

The _____ needs the most paint.

It needs [ ] square units of paint.

Name _____

Date _____

Ref: *Lab Sheet Annotations*, page 304.

● ● ● ● ● T-26

Name_____ Date_____

In each design below find the area of the shaded parts.

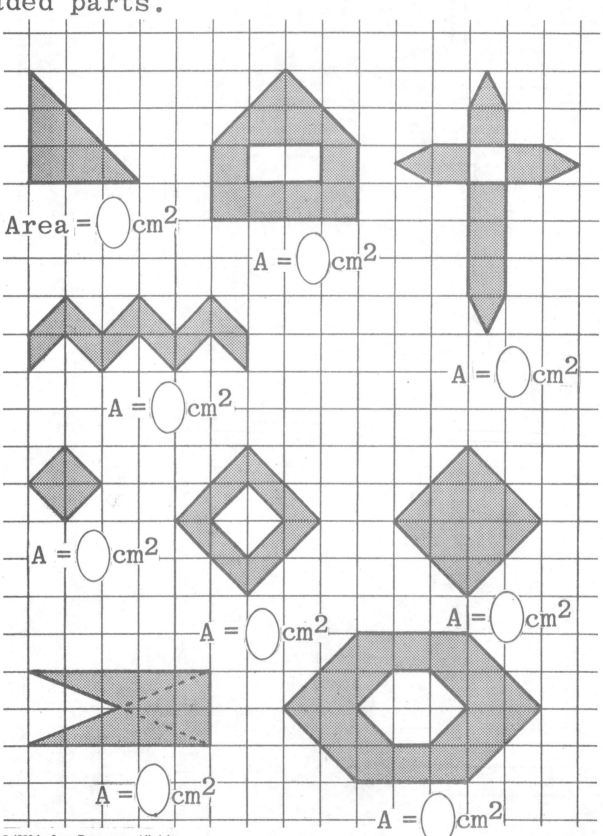

Area = ◯ cm²

A = ◯ cm²

A = ◯ cm²

A = ◯ cm²

A = ◯ cm²

A = ◯ cm²

A = ◯ cm²

A = ◯ cm²

A = ◯ cm²

••••• T-27

			How?
T 20 units	L 5 units	F 3 units	
Measure out			
10 units			
6 units			
8 units			
2 units			
1 unit			
28 units			
16 units			
15 units			
4 units			

Look how much each cup can hold. Pretend that you have a water faucet and a sink.

The example shows you that when you fill B and then fill A from B, there will be five units of water left in A.

			How many units
A 4 units	B 9 units	C 12 units	
Measure out			
A			
B - A			5 units
C - B			
A + B			
C - A			
B - 2A			
C + (B - A)			

Make some papers of your own like this one.

Ref: *Lab Sheet Annotations*, page 305.

MILLIMETERS

centimeters

millimeters

The black rod is __7__ centimeters long; __7__ cm.

The black rod is __70__ millimeters long; __70__ mm.

7 cm = 70 mm

The white rod is _____ centimeters long; ___ cm.

The white rod is _____ millimeters long; ___ mm.

The red rod is ⟨ ___ centimeters long.
            ___ millimeters long.

The purple rod is ⟨ ___ cm.
              ___ mm.

The brown rod is ⟨ ___ cm.
              ___ mm.

The _____ rod is ⟨ ___ cm.
              ___ mm.

---

11 cm = ___ mm   99 cm = ___ mm

90 mm = ___ cm   100 cm = ___ mm

90 cm = ___ mm   1 m = ___ mm

Name _____ Date _____

KILOMETERS for long distances

> 1000 meters = 1 kilometer
>
> 1000 m = 1 km

Look at the map of the USA. (Alaska and Hawaii missing)
It tells you how many km it is from
San Francisco to New York by plane and
by car.

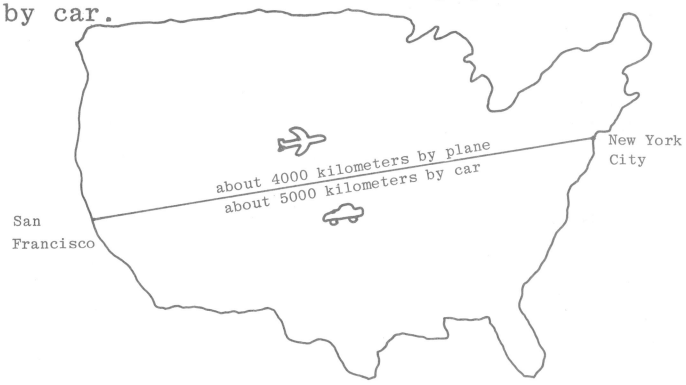

about 4000 kilometers by plane

about 5000 kilometers by car

San Francisco

New York City

An airplane can fly non-stop from New York
to San Francisco in about 4 hours. The trip
is about _____ km. There are no speed limits
in the air.

A car on a highway may not go faster than
100 km an hour. Speed limit 100km/h The trip is about
_____ km long. It will take from _____ days
to a week to get there.

Name _____ Date _____

Make true sentences using < or = or >.

5 m ⊘> 60 cm   24 m ◯ 24000 cm

14 cm ◯ 14 mm   88 mm ◯ 8 cm

5 mm ◯ 50 cm   11 m ◯ 27 cm

50 mm ◯ 5 cm   513 m ◯ 5 km

5 km ◯ 4000 cm   1001 mm ◯ 1 m

200 cm ◯ 3 m   1001 mm ◯ 101 cm

800 m ◯ 1 km   5 km ◯ 5000 m

Choose one.

A banana is about 20   mm (cm) m   km   long.

A river is about 100   mm   cm   m   km   long.

A penpoint is about 1   mm   cm   m   km   wide.

A tall man is about 2   mm   cm   m   km   tall.

A bed is about _____ long.

A grain of rice is about _____ long.

A new baby is about 50 _____ long.

Name

Date

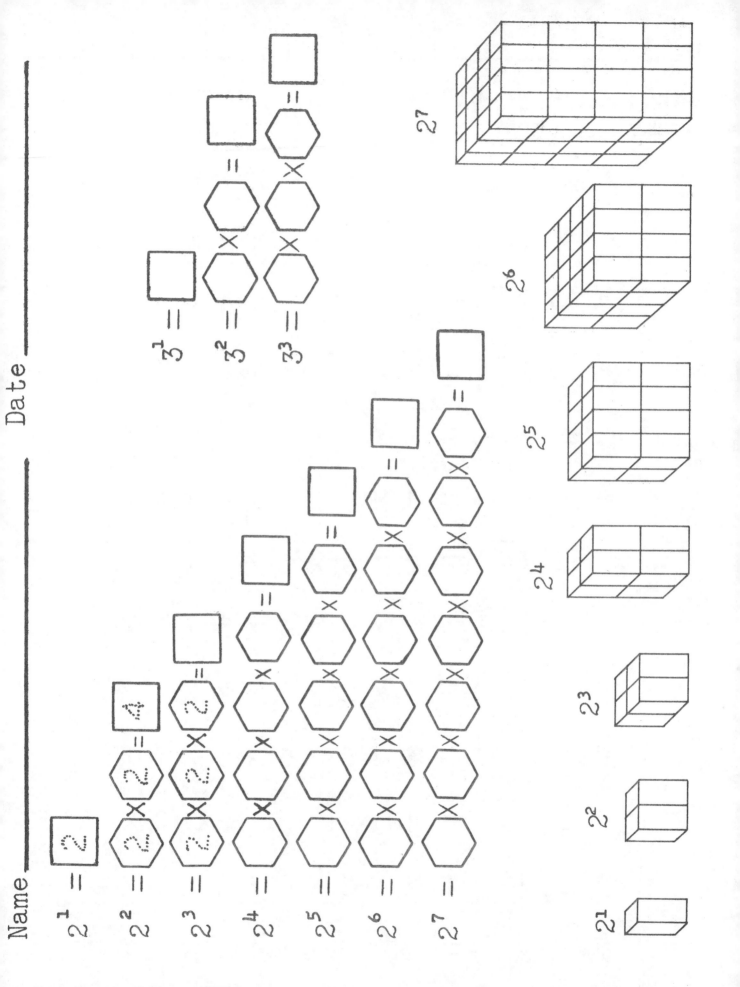

Ref: *Lab Sheet Annotations*, page 312.

● ● ● ● ● U-7

Name _____ Date _____

Make these problems true by crossing
out the extra factors.

1^2 = ⬡(1) = 1 X 1 ~~X 1 X 1 X 1 X 1~~

3^3 = ▢(27) = 3 X 3 X 3 ~~X 3 X 3 X 3~~

5^2 = ⬡ = 5 X 5 X 5 X 5 X 5 X 5

2^1 = ▢ = 2 X 2 X 2 X 2 X 2 X 2

1^4 = ⬡ = 1 X 1 X 1 X 1 X 1 X 1 X 1

4^2 = ▢ = 4 X 4 X 4 X 4 X 4 X 4

5^1 = ⬡ = 5 X 5 X 5 X 5 X 5 X 5

5^3 = ▢ = 5 X 5 X 5 X 5 X 5 X 5

2^3 = ⬡ = 2 X 2 X 2 X 2 X 2 X 2

6^2 = ▢ = 6 X 6 X 6 X 6 X 6 X 6

10^2 = ⬡ = 10 X 10 X 10 X 10 X 10

2^4 = ▢ = 2 X 2 X 2 X 2 X 2 X 2

3^4 = ⬡ = 3 X 3 X 3 X 3 X 3 X 3

Ref: *Lab Sheet Annotations*, page 313.

Name

Date

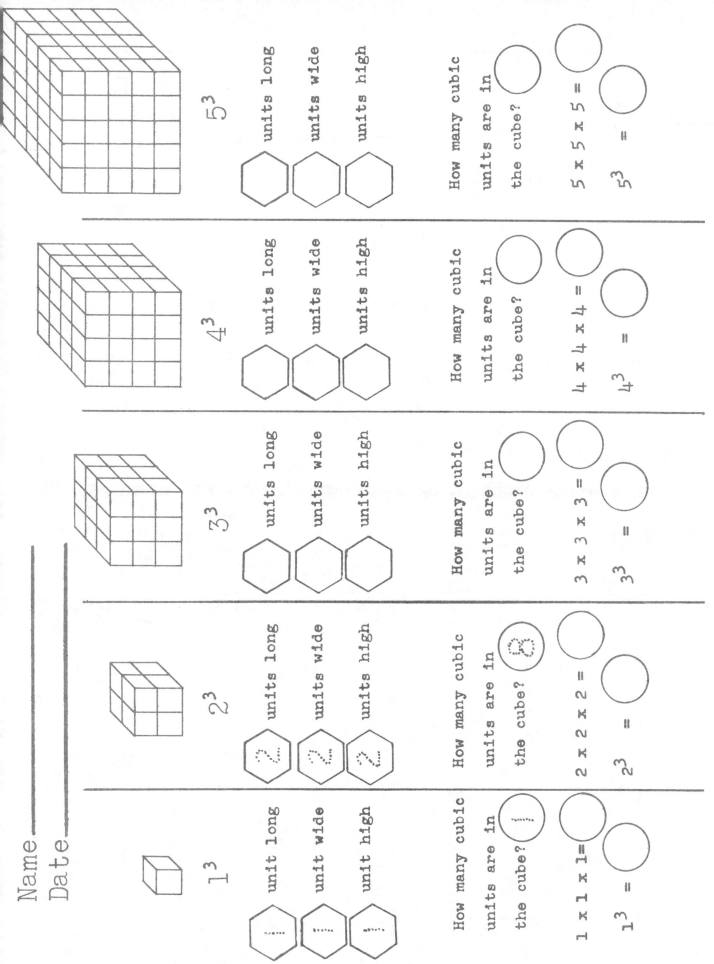

5^3

___ units long

___ units wide

___ units high

How many cubic units are in the cube?

$5 \times 5 \times 5 =$

$5^3 =$

4^3

___ units long

___ units wide

___ units high

How many cubic units are in the cube?

$4 \times 4 \times 4 =$

$4^3 =$

3^3

___ units long

___ units wide

___ units high

How many cubic units are in the cube?

$3 \times 3 \times 3 =$

$3^3 =$

2^3

2 units long

2 units wide

2 units high

How many cubic units are in the cube?

$2 \times 2 \times 2 =$

$2^3 =$

1^3

1 unit long

1 unit wide

1 unit high

How many cubic units are in the cube?

$1 \times 1 \times 1 =$

$1^3 =$

Ref: *Lab Sheet Annotations*, page 313.

● ● ● ● ● U-9

$[\boxed{10}] = 10 = 10^{1}$

$[\boxed{100}] = 10 \times 10 = 10^{2}$

$[\boxed{}] = 10 \times 10 \times 10 = 10^{\bigcirc}$

$[\boxed{}] = 10 \times 10 \times 10 \times 10 = 10^{\bigcirc}$

$[\boxed{}] = 10 \times 10 \times 10 \times 10 \times 10 = 10^{\bigcirc}$

$[\boxed{}] = 10 \times 10 \times 10 \times 10 \times 10 \times 10 = 10^{\bigcirc}$

Match the names for the same number:

10^{5} $10 \times 10 \times 10 \times 10$ 100

10^{4} 10×10 100000

10^{3} $10 \times 10 \times 10 \times 10 \times 10$ 10000

10^{2} $10 \times 10 \times 10$ 1000

10^{6} 10   1000000

10^{1} $10 \times 10 \times 10 \times 10 \times 10 \times 10$ 10

Ref: *Lab Sheet Annotations*, page 313.

• • • • • • U-1(

Name

Date

Directions:
Draw straight lines from each point to every other point. Record the number of lines drawn.

Points	Lines	
1		
2		
3		
4		

Points	Lines	
5		
6		
7		
8		

See if you can figure out the answers to these two problems without even drawing the points or the lines.

• • • • • •U-11

Name _____

Date _____

Be a detective!
Look at the pictures
and write in the answers.

Picture	How many lines?	How many lines from each point?	How many inside lines?	How many intersections?	How many inside intersections?
(5 points, all connected)					
(5 points)					
(4 points with diagonals)	6		2	1	
(triangle, 3 points)		2	0	3	0
(line segment, 2 points)	—	1		0	
(single point)	0	0			

Ref: *Lab Sheet Annotations*, page 315.

••••• U-12

Name _____ Date _____

ARROW GAMES

1	2	3	4	5	6	7	8	9	10
11	12	13	14	15	16	17	18	19	20
21	22	23	24	25	26	27	28	29	30
31	32	33	34	35	36	37	38	39	40
41	42	43	44	45	46	47	48	49	50
51	52	53	54	55	56	57	58	59	60
61	62	63	64	65	66	67	68	69	70
71	72	73	74	75	76	77	78	79	80
81	82	83	84	85	86	87	88	89	90
91	92	93	94	95	96	97	98	99	100

54 ↑ → ↘   is the same thing as   54 - 10 + 1 + 11

13 → → →   is the same thing as   13

77 ↗ ↗   is the same thing as   77

25 ← ↓ ↓   is the same thing as   _____ in arrows

36 + 9 + 9   is the same thing as   36 _____ in arrows

4 + 1 - 1 + 10 - 10   is the same thing as   _____

◯ ↗ ↗ ↗   is the same thing as   _____

◯ ↓ ↓ ↙ ←   is the same thing as   _____

Ref: *Lab Sheet Annotations*, page 320.

Name _____ Date _____

Please simplify the following
                    TRICKY arrow problems:

TRICKY   SIMPLE

↓↑↑→   ↗

↑↓↑

↑↑←←

↑↓↑↓↑↓↑

→→↓←←

→←

↗↗↑→↘

↓←→↑

Ref: *Lab Sheet Annotations*, page 320.

Name _____ Date _____

From: 150   To:
Philadelphia   kilometers   New York

Train speed: 100 kilometers per hour (km/h)

The train will travel ☐ hrs. and ☐ min.

From: Philadelphia

To: Chicago

1200 kilometers

Speed:

☐
km/h

The non-stop plane gets to Chicago in
2 hours.
Its speed is _____ kilometers per hour.

---

210 km to Washington

Philadelphia ↗

Speed:

☐

The Bing family drove to Washington in
$3\frac{3}{4}$ hours. They stopped for gas for 10 min.
They stopped 35 minutes for lunch.
What was their speed? _____ km/h

Ref: *Lab Sheet Annotations*, page 338.

•••••• X-15

$1\frac{1}{2}$ hours = ☐ minutes

3 hours = ☐ minutes

$2\frac{1}{4}$ hours = ☐ minutes

6 hours = ☐ minutes

12 hours = ☐ minutes

$1\frac{2}{3}$ hours = ☐ minutes

30 minutes = ◯ hour

45 minutes = ◯ hour

75 minutes = ◯ hour

1 minute = ◯ hour

7 minutes = ◯ hour

10 minutes = ◯ hour

Ref: *Lab Sheet Annotations*, page 338.

●●●●● X-16